Institute for the Study of
Natural Horse Care Practices

Natural Trim Training Program

A Foundational Course in the

Fundamentals of the Natural Trim – Principles and Practice

Leading to the Recognition of One's Status as

"ISNHCP Practitioner"

Sanctioned Jointly by the
Institute for the Study of
Natural Horse Care Practices (ISNHCP)
and the
Association for the Advancement of
Natural Horse Care Practices (AANHCP)

In Accordance with the Laws of Nature
as Exemplified by the Unfettered Lifestyles and Hooves
of our Model, the
Wild, Free-Roaming Horse
of the United States Great Basin

Jaime Jackson

ISNHCP Clinician
Author, *The Natural Horse: Lessons from the Wild*

For further information:

NHC Press – an imprint of J. Jackson Publishing
P.O. Box 1432
Lompoc, CA 93436
NHCPressInfo@gmail.com

ISBN-13: 978-0-9848399-5-7

Table of Contents & Study Assignments

Table of Contents & Study Assignments (cont'd)

Practicums — Post Step 1 Training Steps

Appendices

Introduction

This "basic" *Natural Trim Training Program* is a comprehensive, academic, and hands-on foundational course in the artful science of natural hoof care (NHC). The natural trim is a humane, barefoot trimming method that *mimics the natural wear patterns of wild, free-roaming horses* (aka, the "mustang") of the U.S. Great Basin. This action immediately "triggers" healthy growth patterns, that, when accompanied by other natural holistic practices also based on the wild horse model, eventually result in naturally shaped hooves. By all accounts, this transformation is truly a miracle of nature, but, technically, it is an outcome of the specie's adaptation, embedded in the DNA of every horse living today. It is of paramount importance to recognize that practitioners do not force the foot to look a certain way (e. g., like a wild horse hoof), but facilitate it through the natural trim method of mimicking wild horse hoof wear patterns.

Students enrolled in the training program learn the basics of the natural trim. Which is to say the emphasis is on trimming hooves not complicated by *extreme capsule deformity*. Many years of experience has shown the ISNHCP that such deformity, the outcome of neglect, misguided hoof care methods, and deep pathology, only create confusion in the minds of beginning students. The "basics" of natural trim mechanics become mired and lost in the overwhelming complications of dealing with severely troubled hooves. The ISNHCP recognizes that until basic natural trim mechanics are clearly understood and mastered on hooves suffering minimal deformity, the path to resolving the complexities of extreme deformity is virtually untenable. One must "learn to crawl before one learns to walk." Indeed, to tackle the worst deformed hooves imaginable, the trimmer must not only be sound in the basics, but academically prepared through advanced training to facilitate complex mass changes in concert with the laws of nature. To this end, the ISNHCP is creating an *Advanced Natural Trim Training Program* with its own training requirements that build upon the basics taught in the introductory course. The course is scheduled for availability to those qualified in late 2017.

capsule – a tough horny covering that protects the ends of the toes of numerous plant-eating 4-footed mammals such as the horse

4 Pillars of NHC

The basic natural trim is taught within the context of the *Four Pillars of natural horse care (NHC)*. These pillars are the foundations of natural care based on the

One of my base camps in central Nevada, U.S. Great Basin, c. early 1984. (AANHCP Archives)

wild horse model. They include *natural boarding, natural horsemanship, a reasonably natural diet, and the natural trim* itself. Years of experience have also shown that it is impossible to conduct a natural trim consistently with full import independently of the other three pillars. As an example, a horse fed a diet that causes inflammation and degradation of hoof structure will continue to do so regardless of the practitioner's diligence in carrying out natural trim mechanics.

The official ISNHCP trimming guidelines are based on the wild horse research conducted by myself in the 1980s in the U.S. Great Basin. When properly adhered to, these guidelines will serve to prevent mistakes that harm the horse and the hooves.

Overview of training steps

As explained on the ISNHCP website, this training program includes both academic and hands-on instruction. This includes quizzes intended to be used by you as learning aids, submitted written exams enabling the ISNHCP to evaluate your understanding of required subject matter, and a continuous stream of field evaluations of performance by clinicians and field instructors throughout the course of your training. Students must demonstrate evidence of competency at each stage of their training if they are to proceed to the next step. All along the way, training reports are filed by your teachers with ISNHCP headquarters. The ISNHCP authorizes students to proceed with training, or to return to previous steps for *reme-*

remediation – actions that bring about a correction

diation, based on these reports. This system of accountability protects horses and you. Our goal is to produce competent, professional hoof care practitioners who represent the AANHCP/ISNHCP vital mission in the field.

The importance of academics and studying

The remainder of this training manual provides you with details of the training steps and course materials. It also includes foundational information about the history and science of the natural trim, descriptions of the various structures that comprise the horse's foot, and a brief stepwise discussion of the natural trim itself. Further, this manual includes specific study assignments with quizzes taken from required ISNHCP learning materials you are provided with following your initial tuition payment. This is important information you need to learn by way of *independent study* and, later, apply in the field under the direct tutelage of your clinicians and field instructors. Here, we need to make an important distinction between "reading" and "studying."

Course learning materials are intended to be *studie*d rather than simply *perused* (lightly read or glanced over). This is because a full and complete mastery of the natural trim is not possible simply through trim mechanics. Academics are equally, if not more, important! Indeed, the inherent complexities of the foot's biology requires an understanding of the underlying "laws of nature" if the trim itself is to be executed effectively, humanely, and consistently from year to year throughout the horse's life. Accordingly, this training program includes a system of verification and accountability at all levels of instruction, including academics, to make sure that the student knows what they are doing and why.

Helpful hint #1 – Use a dictionary. If you come across words you are unfamiliar with, get yourself a dictionary. Look the word up! See how it is used in the context it is written. A true academic doesn't try to "slide by" with word meaning, but visits the dictionary often in order to understand what the writer is saying. I've helped you here and there defining some words (in *italics*) alongside the main text in this training manual.

Not surprising, you will come across many new words that you won't find in the dictionary, or whose meaning is different than what the dictionary has published. This is because NHC has its own language, replete with words that apply specifically to what we do. In these instances, NHC definitions are provided. Your job is to learn these new words, and, as you progress with your training, discover how they apply to what we do and why. Farriers, for example, won't understand what you're saying in many instances because their language is different than our own. This is because our understanding of the hoof and what we do to it as practitioners is different than theirs and what they do. Much of our language is also new to horse owners. One of your tasks will be to explain to them those terms that will be useful as caring horse owners who want to act on the 4 Pillars of NHC. It's not very useful, however, to try to explain to them all of the technical things we do. Most of the time, they just need reassurance, and to be pointed to the 4 Pillars. Directing them to some of our NHC books is another useful way to help them understand.

Helpful hint #2 — Use the quizzes as teaching aids. I've sprinkled quizzes throughout the training manual so that you can test yourself on your understanding of the study materials. This is an excellent way to learn. I did it all the time I was in college as a science major. You'll see that I've divided the manual into the various training steps, and, where useful, further divided each step into various related sections (similar to chapters in a book), Part 1, Part 2, etc. Most of these sections will have a quiz. *Here's what you do with the quizzes:*

After studying each section, take the quiz (if there is one). Write down your answers. Of course, if you can't come up with an answer, it simply means you've got to study up some more. Review the study materials again. When you finally have all your answers written down — but not before! (you're only cheating yourself!) — go to the answer key at the back of the manual and see how you did. I usually provide a short discussion about the answer's subject matter if warranted. Study that too. Now if you miss an answer — go immediately back into the appropriate learning materials and hunt down where the correct answer came from. I usually cite where that is. Understand, this checking on yourself is hard work. But, if you do this faithfully, you'll soon begin to understand how I want you to approach the information, and also how I want you to understand it. It's a way of disciplining your mind, which will transfer to your professionalism as a practitioner in the field. Learning how to learn is a process unto itself.

Helpful hint #3 — Form a study group with other students. There were many times during my college years that studying the quizzes fell short. Sometimes, I just couldn't "get it," no matter what. I needed someone to help me understand what the heck the teacher was asking for. I begin to scout around for other classmates who (invariably) wore the same confused faces as me. Not surprisingly, they were as anxious as me to get together to figure things out. We would usually meet at my place for our private study hall, never more than a small group of 3 or 4 of us. Invariably (once again), one of us had figured out an answer that the rest of us couldn't for whatever reason. And importantly, explaining themselves at the student level, we could hash out an understanding of our own. Once we got through the quizzes (provided to us by our instructor, just like I've provided you in the training manual), we'd celebrate with a round of cards and snacks. What might have been a miserable learning experience on our own leading to failure, we turned into "fun," each of us concerned that everyone understood the answers. I'll never forget those days, and actually miss our get togethers. Well, you can do the same. As I explained on the ISNHCP website, you can form your own study groups by going to the ISNHCP Student Facebook page and recruiting others to join you. Because our students are coming from all around the world, you can use the Internet to get together via Skype or Webinar. I tell you, if I were a student, I would be there right now beckoning others to join me!

Helpful hint #4 – Register for an ISNHCP Webinar Study Hall. To be perfectly honest, now and then in those study groups none of us could figure out the answers to the questions. When this happened, we marched as a group into the instructor's office (by appointment, of course) and pleaded our ignorance. A discussion would occur there that led to at least one of us to understand the answer or solution. But that person was always able to explain it so that the rest of us got it at the next study session at my place. Not the easiest path to take, but one that works when you're really motivated to learn. So, if you or your study group gets stumped (an American idiom for "I don't understand"), it may be time to get yourselves into my online Webinar office. Check out the ISNHCP Student Store drop-down menu for my office hours. I'll be waiting for you.

In summary

This training manual is your road map to becoming a qualified student practitioner serving horses and their owners, fully sanctioned by both the ISNHCP and AANHCP. Keep it with you throughout all of your training and study it often, including it's learning assignments. *Our ISNHCP philosophy is to learn, learn, learn!* Our model requires this of us, not just during your basic training, but beyond into your working life as a professional.

AANHCP Oath, Disciplinary Policy, and 4 Guiding Principles of the Natural Trim

The natural trim is taught using proven trim mechanics based on the wild horse model. I believe that any method based on this genuine natural model should not lose its connection to the very animal from which the method is derived. Losing that connection threatens the very foundations of the natural trim and NHC generally. The natural trim, in other words, could be interpreted to mean anything, and with potentially serious consequences for domesticated horses. To clarify and enforce the model, the method, and the ethical practices of the ISNHCP, including its clinicians, instructors, practitioners, and students insofar as they may impact domesticated horses, the ISNHCP has adopted three important documents created by the founders of the AANHCP. These are the *Disciplinary Policy of the AANHCP*, the *Oath of Allegiance to the AANHCP Vital Mission*, and the *4 Guiding Principles of the Natural Trim*. The *DP* and *Oath* can be found in pdf on the DVD; the *4 Guiding Principles* are discussed below and elsewhere in your learning materials. A brief summary of each are included below:

Disciplinary Policy of the AANHCP & ISNHCP

Briefly, the "DP" is a set of rules and guidelines that were drawn up with the aid of an attorney that spell out the legal responsibilities of the AANHCP to protect its vital mission, members, and horses in our care, all in keeping with the *AANHCP Oath of Allegiance.*

Oath of Allegiance to the AANHCP-ISNHCP Vital Mission

The AANHCP Oath is largely based on the Hippocratic Oath, traced to the Ancient Greek physician, Hippocrates of Kos. The oath is significant for two important admonitions: "First, do no harm," and "Respect the healing powers of nature."

Hippocrates, "Father of Modern Medicine" (460 BC - 370 c. BC)

Implicit in both the AANHCP Oath and the AANHCP DP is that no system of calculated harm will be brought by members upon any horse. The second admonition applies to any calculated practice or method that obstructs or prevents the horse's body from healing naturally. In either case, the DP provides for the investigation and expulsion of violators from the AANHCP membership when such actions are proven. This also applies to students in the ISNHCP training program.

4 Guiding Principles of the Natural Trim

The *4 Guiding Principles of the Natural Trim* are admonitions that reinforce the AANHCP Oath by embedding the hoof's natural state in natural trim mechanics:

1. **Leave that which naturally should be there as seen in the wild.**
2. **Remove only that which is naturally worn away in the wild.**
3. **Allow to grow that which should be there naturally as seen in the wild, but isn't due to human meddling.**
4. **Ignore all pathology.**

The first three principles are founded upon the hoof's natural wear patterns I observed in the wild, rather than in a technical language that describe trim mechanics devoid of any relationship to the wild horse model. My purpose in doing this was to protect the integrity of the natural trim from fraud by making sure that any interpretation given by AANHCP members to natural trim mechanics must not violate the inherent laws of nature demonstrated by the wild horse hoof in its natural state.

The fourth guiding principle admonishes the trimmer to ignore the many symptoms of pathology that typically plague the hooves of domesticated horses. Experience has shown that by "un-focusing" the mind on domestication's deleterious effects during trimming, and instead visualizing the outcome of nature's healing powers, execution of trim mechanics invariably harmonized more precisely with the other three guiding principles. "Giving into pathology," I often warn students, "invites the myths and mishaps of convention to enter trim mechanics, thereby causing harm." Responding to critics that "ignoring all pathology" contradicts common sense and invites the progression of disease, my response always flows from the tenets of the AANHCP (Hippocratic) Oath – Healing unfolds when we seriously embrace and act on the *4 Pillars of NHC*. Pathology invariably takes care of itself when we do the right thing and "respect the healing powers of nature."

Study Assignment
AANHCP Oath, DP, and 4 Guiding Principles

- Read all three documents, as these are your contract with the ISNHCP and, upon posting to the AANHCP website as a sanctioned practitioner, the AANHCP as well.

Step 1 – ISNHCP Training Program

Independent Study

Part 1: The Wild Horse and the Natural Trim

Origins of the horse and the natural trim

As stated in this training manual's *Introduction*, the 4 Pillars of NHC have their origins in the wild horse model. This is significant because my research has shown that the lifestyles of wild, free-roaming horses inhabiting the U.S. Great Basin are conducive to exemplary health and sound, naturally shaped hooves. With this premise, I felt confident in extending this model to domesticated horses in my care, which, among other things of importance discussed later in this manual, led directly to a method of trimming that is now proven and humane. This method, strengthened by time and numerous innovations, provides the precise guidelines for conducting the basic natural trim taught in the ISNHCP training program today.

The question arises, however, why would the wild hoof serve as a "model" when domesticated horses aren't wild? The answer is actually logical: other than lifestyles, both are exactly the same species. Paleo scientists using sophisticated genetic ("mitochondrialDNA")[1] markers have studied the evolutionary biology of the horse and determined that today's "modern" horse, *Equus ferus caballus*, is genetically indistinguishable from their wild, pre-domesticated ancestor, *Equus ferus ferus*. Thus, it is highly significant that the species we know today arrived through evolutionary descent over one million years ago; and, that the wild horse of the U.S. Great Basin, provides us with a clear vision of what that adaptation means as a model of enduring stability for natural hoof care.

It is interesting, and a testimony to the overriding power of natural selection, that all of the domestication humans have heaped upon the horse over the past 10,000 years has not changed what nature created long before our two species ever began to mingle at the dawn of domestication. In fact, the very method of natural hoof care taught by the ISNHCP is based upon this premise. I still find it hard to believe that, until I conducted my wild horse research literally thousands of years after the first horse was domesticated, the scientific basis for the "natural trim"

[1]mtDNA is a powerful genetic tool for tracking ancestry through females.

was both unpublished and unknown. The good news is that, for the first time since the first metal shoe was nailed to a horse's foot one thousand years ago in *medieval* Europe, the inhumane practice of horseshoeing no longer reigns unchallenged. The artful science of natural hoof care is now practiced in nearly every continent on this planet, benefiting horses of every breed and equestrian discipline. It is a revolution that is not going away as long as there are caring human beings.

medieval – also called the "Middle Ages." In this case, middle means "between the Roman empire and the Renaissance"–that is, after the fall of the great Roman state and before the "rebirth" of culture that we call the Renaissance. This same period used to be called the "Dark Ages", since it was believed that in these years civilization all but vanished. And indeed, for most Europeans in these centuries, it was a time of poverty, famine, plague, and superstition.

Study Assignments
"Origins of the horse and the natural trim"

Your task now is to understand the facts underlying the viability of the wild, free-roaming horse of the U.S. Great Basin as our model for domestic horse care, particularly at the hoof. The time to start studying has arrived! Go through each of the study assignments below. You might find it helpful to keep a workbook and take notes along the way, to keep yourself organized and focused. I find it useful to add paper tabs on the pages of books I'm studying for quick reference. Take the quiz that follows the assignments. Use the key in the appendix to check your answers, *after you've committed them to paper.* Remember, if you just go straight to the key for the answers, you won't learn a thing unless others do the thinking for you, which pretty much ends in the real world that lies ahead! You're teaching yourself mental discipline which you will also need for the Step 1 Online Exam!

Study Assignment #1 – *The Natural Horse: Foundations for Natural Horsemanship.* Jaime Jackson

– This is an important book to study from front to back with a critical eye. It represents my observations of our model's life in the wild, a bit of their history, lots on the hooves, and other areas of interest to you. Experience has taught me that this book really requires guided reading. So, for our immediate purposes, study the following along with my introductory comments:

- **Introduction, Chapter 1, and Chapter 2** – Not too much to cover, but important, foundational information about our model.

Study Assignment #2 – Power Point Lectures

– More important information that augments Assignment #1. Take your time and be sure to enjoy the many photos of our model.

- **"Overview of NHC"** – 123 slides that cover lots of good information about what we do, photos of wild horses and more about their Paleo history, and also examples of the natural trim I've added in for comparative purposes.

- **"Evolution and Adaptation of *Equus ferus caballus*"** – 20 slides, very brief discussion of how scientists think natural selection works.

Study Assignment #3 – *Wild Horses as Native North American Wildlife.* (Revised, January 2010) by J.F. Kirkpatrick, Ph.D. and P. M. Fazio, Ph.D.

– Study this paper closely in its entirety as it provides important science-based information about the genetic history of our model that *corroborates* my own research findings detailed in my book, *The Natural Horse*. As a reading, it isn't too *heady* as it was targeted by its authors for the lay public wanting to learn more about our wild horses and their political plight. Many special interests are now either lobbying to get rid of them altogether or manipulate their breeding habits in ways that truly clash with natural selection. They also refute those who claim wild horses are an "invasive species" that have no justifiable right to inhabit Great Basin public lands. This document can be found in the DVD included with your learning materials.

corroborate – to support with evidence or authority

heady – intellectually stimulating or demanding

Study Assignment #4 – *The Natural Trim: Principles and Practice.* Jaime Jackson

– This book was my attempt to cover a lot of NHC territory in one place. It's written in two parts, as the title implies. Part 1 lays out the principles of natural hoof care, including a brief history of NHC; Part 2 gets into what we do as practitioners, plus some examples of how our NHC guidelines are applied to trimming a range of very healthy to very troubled hooves. You'll be spending a bit of your time in it, so we might as well get started now.

- **Preface and Introduction to Part 1: "What is Natural Hoof Care (NHC)."** – Not too much to cover, but important foundational information about our model. Your reading assignment begins on page *xi* and continues to page 29. This will give you important historical background on NHC and what we do today, and what we hope to accomplish in the future. Some of the key players in our organization's history show up in some of the pictures. These and others are those who came before you, making your own journey possible.

- **Chapter 1: "The Perfectly Natural Hoof."** — More very important foundational material that explains where our model came from in his ancient past. It knits in closely with your previous study assignments.

Quiz (True or False)
"Origins of the horse and the natural trim"

1. Jackson's studies of wild horses included horses living in the U.S. Great Basin, but did not include horses living outside of the U.S. Great Basin.
2. The Wild and Free-Roaming Horses and Burros Act of 1971 was the first federal legislation passed to protect America's wild horses.
3. The modern horse evolved in N. America over a million years ago, but around 8 to 10,000 years ago, became extinct with many other large mammals. Europeans re-introduced them during the Age of Discovery 500 years ago.
4. The first wild, free-roaming horse populations in the Great Basin appeared after 1850, when the region became part of the United States after the Mexican Cessation of 1848.
5. Jackson's hoof studies at the BLM corrals studied the effects of 125 years of adaptation in the U.S. Great Basin.
6. The word "feral" is a human *appellation* that has little biological meaning except in transitory behavior, usually forced on the animal as when stalled.

Appellation — an identifying name or title

7. *Natural hoof care* and the *natural trim* mean the same thing.
8. NHC can trace its roots to the classic text, *Art of Horsemanship*, written by the Ancient Greek General Xenophon, 350 BC.
9. Not all wild or feral horse herds are suitable models for NHC.
10. From the standpoint of adaptation, the only distinguishing difference between wild, free-roaming horses of the U.S. Great Basin and a horse living in a stall 24/7 is *experience*.

A-force — The Adaptation Force

The evolutionary descent of *E. ferus caballus* through natural selection brings with it a powerful, although unseen, force embedded in the animal's DNA. What this force means is that a "horse is a horse," and, contrary to what may be ascribed to the horse *anthropomorphistically* or by *humanization*, there is nothing we can do to change the fact. In NHC science, we call this the *adaptation force* (A-force). Called "telos" by the ancient Greeks, the A-force is what nature *selected* the horse to be, long before early tribes of humans came along to hunt, and then domesticate, them. This force cannot be changed by selective breeding, horse abuse, horseshoeing, or even the natural trim! It's what makes the horse "what he is." Yet, the A-force has its limits . . .

anthropomorphism — an interpretation of what is not human or personal in terms of human or personal characteristics

humanization — attributing human qualities to

In early post-*Pleistocene* North America 8,000 – 10,000 years ago, *E. ferus ferus*, not yet domesticated by humans, along with many other *megafauna*, became extinct. I believe this extinction was due, in part, to the horse's inability to adapt to apparent changes in the environment caused by global warming. It is entirely plausible that retreating glaciers spawned sugar-rich grasses in their wake that many ungulates (hoofed animals) besides the horse could not digest. This lead to unprecedented levels of a debilitating and life-threatening disease NHC science defines as *Whole Horse Inflammatory Disease* (WHID).

Pleistocene — geologic era dating from 2.5 million 11,700 years ago

megafauna — animals (as bears, bison, or mammoths) of particularly large size

WHID expresses itself symptomatically throughout the horse's body as a range of metabolic disorders consistent with *metabolic syndrome*,[1] including digestive problems like colic, obesity, abnormal hair growth, organ failure, inflammation of the feet,[2] and lameness. *Incapacitated* to move naturally would have attracted the many megafauna predators of the time, including tribes of *Paleolithic* humans, lions (now extinct), and saber-toothed tigers (also extinct). Disease, the changing flora not compatible with the horse's adaptation, and the resulting large scale disruption of normal prey-predator relationships, could very well have contributed to or precipitated the massive extinction event that irreversibly took its toll on the A-force of many species who depended on each other.

incapacitated – unable to work, move, or function in the usual way

Paleolithic – of or relating to the earliest period of the Stone Age characterized by rough or chipped stone implements

Earlier migrations of *E. ferus ferus* from North America to Mongolia and Eurasia — regions more distant from melting glaciers — spared the species from total

[1]A syndrome marked by the presence of usually three or more of a group of factors (as high blood pressure, abdominal obesity, high triglyceride levels, low HDL levels, and high fasting levels of blood sugar) that are linked to an increased risk of cardiovascular disease and type 2 diabetes—called also *insulin resistance syndrome*

[2]Widely known as *Laminitis*. Thought to be a disease of the foot, laminitis is actually a *symptom* of WHID.

extinction. Surviving equine families of *E. ferus ferus* then mingled with Eurasian tribes of *Homo sapien sapien,* our human *Neolithic* ancestors, who, according to scientists, domesticated the horse as early as 6,000 years ago in Ukraine and Kazakhstan. Arguably, both species needed each other in a rapidly developing and ever-complicated "civilized" world.

Neolithic – of or relating to the latest period of the Stone Age characterized by polished stone implements and the beginning of agriculture

Summary

The A-force, powered by millions of years of evolutionary descent before the dawn of our own species, has survived in the horse to this day. *And this includes the horse's hoof.* I first observed the effect of the A-force in the wild. And through the development of new NHC science and its technical applications, I discovered how it manifested itself *commensurately* in the hooves of domesticated horses. Students have heard me say in my training clinics, the "force is with you" when conducting the natural trim, especially within the broad context of the 4 Pillars of NHC. This point brings us, however, to a significant, if not defining, limitation of the natural trim all students of NHC should fully understand. *The natural trim does not create naturally shaped hooves.* As in the wild, naturally shaped hooves are "shaped" by the lifestyle of the animal. Much more on this later in your study assignments.

commensurate – corresponding in size, extent, amount, or degree

Study assignments
A-force - the Adaptation Force

Study Assignment #1 – *The Healing Angle: Nature's Gateway to the Healing Field.* Jaime Jackson

This study assignment moves us away from the adaptation of the horse in geological and genetic terms, and brings us to the present – explaining why today's U.S. Great Basin wild horse is a viable model for NHC, and specifically, why the A-force applies to the hooves in ways that are of fundamental importance to the natural trim. Much of the content of the *Healing Angle: Nature's Gateway to the Healing Field,* is pretty advanced stuff for an introductory course in natural hoof care. But the early chapters are accessible to the beginner and are important reading. These chapters discuss the A-force within the context of the "healing powers of nature" and how I came to understand and use it during the developmental stages of our NHC science. The A-force is also the door-opener to what we call the *Healing Angle of Growth* (H°), the foundational hoof measurement upon which natural trim is based. Since you will be learning about H° later in the training manual, I think this is a good place to learn where it came from. But unless you want to get really confused, don't venture into the other chapters. I recommend that once you finish Chapter 3, put the book aside for now. We'll return to a few more select parts a little later in your studies, but after we've laid some more groundwork. So, for our immediate purposes, study the following:

- **Chapters 1 through 3.**

Naturally shaped hooves in the U.S. Great Basin

Early on in my field studies of wild horses I learned that the exemplary – healthy and naturally shaped – hooves I observed everywhere were created by the animals themselves. This was achieved simply as a consequence of the way they lived out their lives in family units in the rugged terrain of the high desert biome of the U.S. Great Basin. This "behavior driven" movement was clearly central to the A-force of the species. Later, as I observed entire wild horse families removed by government "gathers" from their native *home ranges* – for the purposes of population control on public lands – and then confined to long term government corrals to live out their lives, the exemplary quality of their hooves corrupted and no longer resembled what existed in the wild. The A-force, I reasoned, was still resident in the hooves via the specie's DNA, but not *omnipresent* as it was in the home ranges. Concluding that lifestyle was the specific trigger to bring forth the A-force, I then turned my attention to client horses to prove this. The science of natural hoof care was about to be borne!

home range – the area to which an animal usually confines its daily activities

omnipresent – present in all places at all times

While my books and other written materials are replete with images of wild horse hooves, I've decided to include images of freeze-dried cadaver specimens in this training manual (*Overleaf* – next four pages). I have shared these biospecimens in every natural trim clinic since I procured them with the BLM's help over 35 years ago. The horses that wore these perished in BLM gathers, but they perfectly represent what are genuinely naturally shaped hooves. As I've told others down through the years, any purported law of nature advanced by any person characterizing a naturally shaped hoof must be consistent with these hooves. In *Step 1-Part 4* of this training manual, we will look closer at the shape characteristics of the natural hoof with an eye to how we will mimic them as trimmers.

Overleaf – images of Great Basin wild, free-roaming horse hooves (cadaver biospecimens) →

(Continued on page 24)

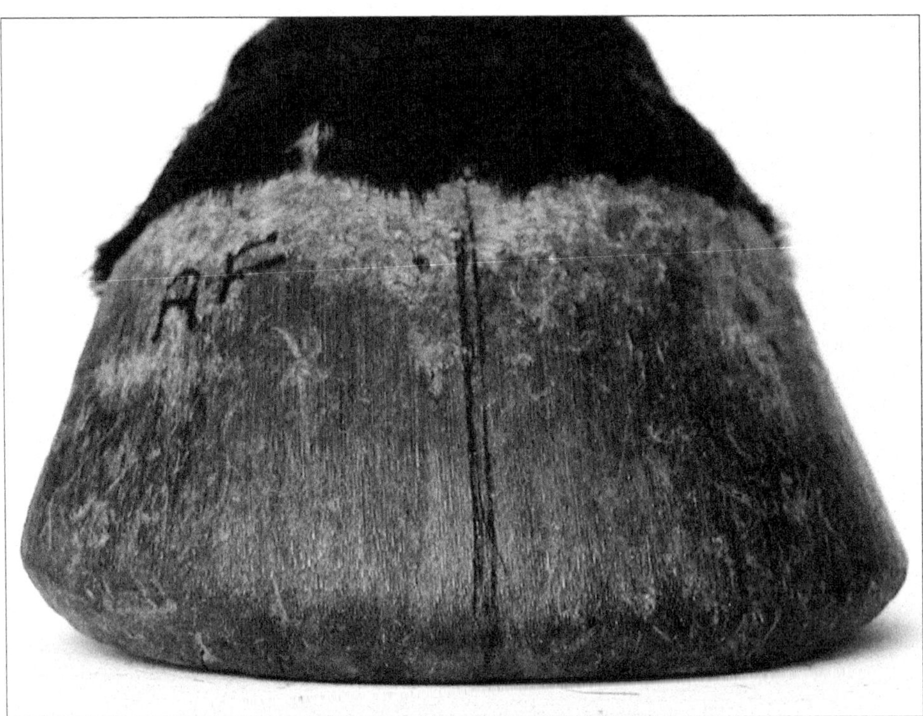

Right front, mediolateral view – wild hoof (U.S Great Basin)

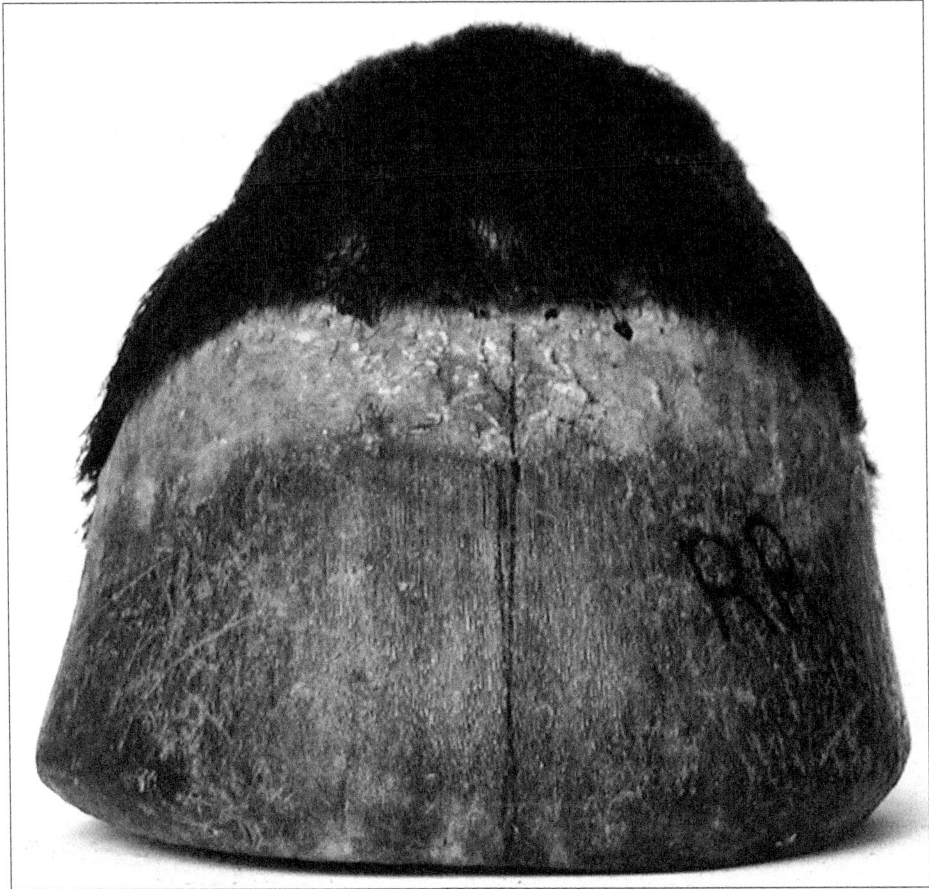

Right hind, mediolateral view – wild hoof (U.S Great Basin)

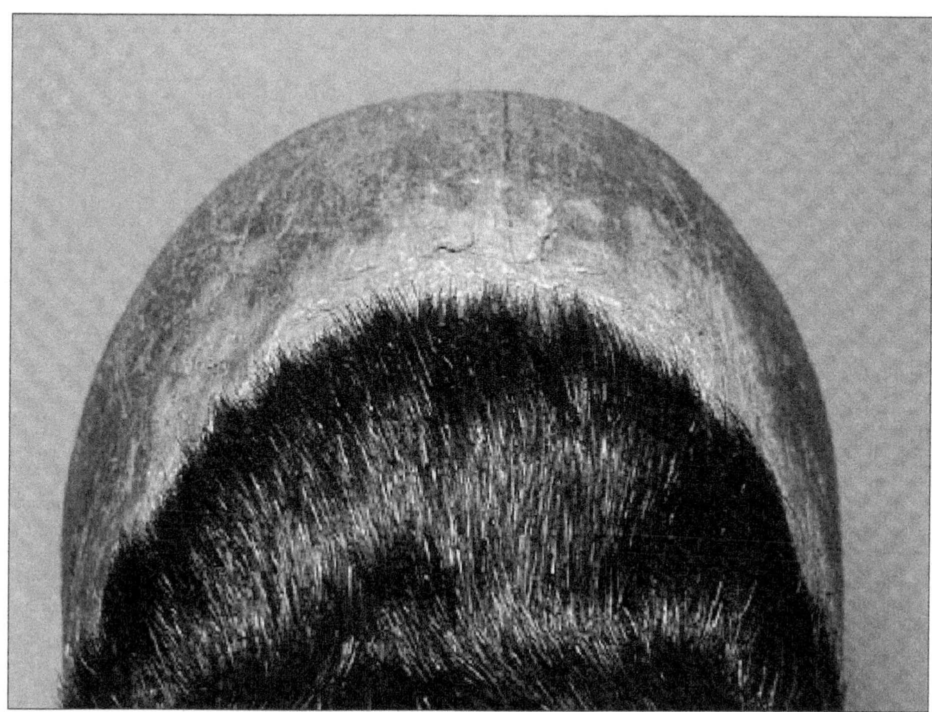

Left hind, superior view, wild hoof (U.S Great Basin)

Left front, lateral view – wild hoof (U.S Great Basin)

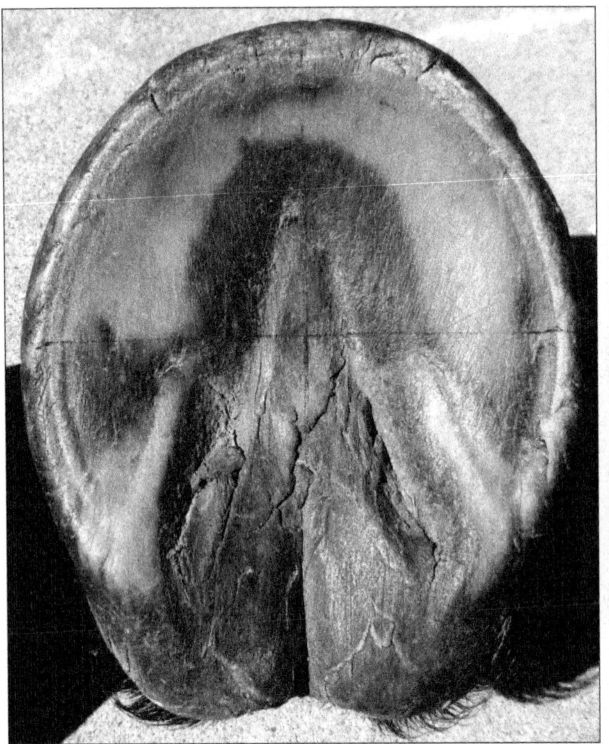

Right front, volar view, wild hoof (U.S Great Basin)

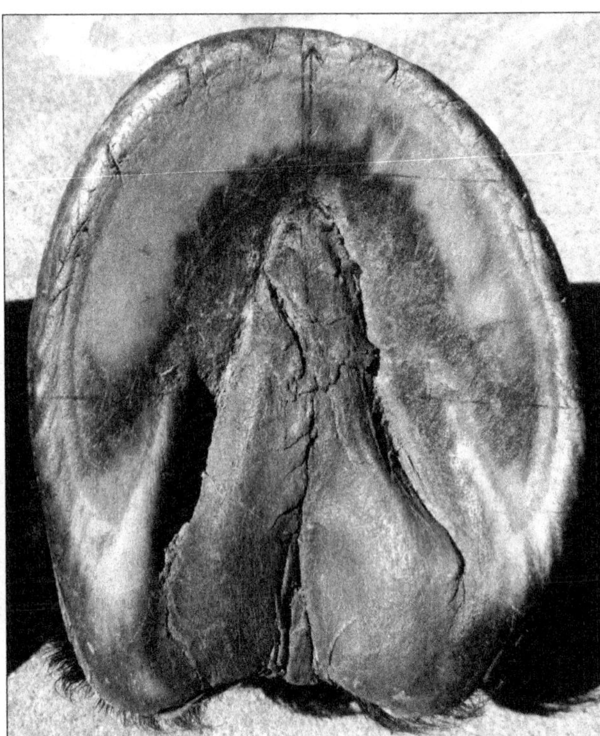

Left hind, volar view, wild hoof (U.S Great Basin)

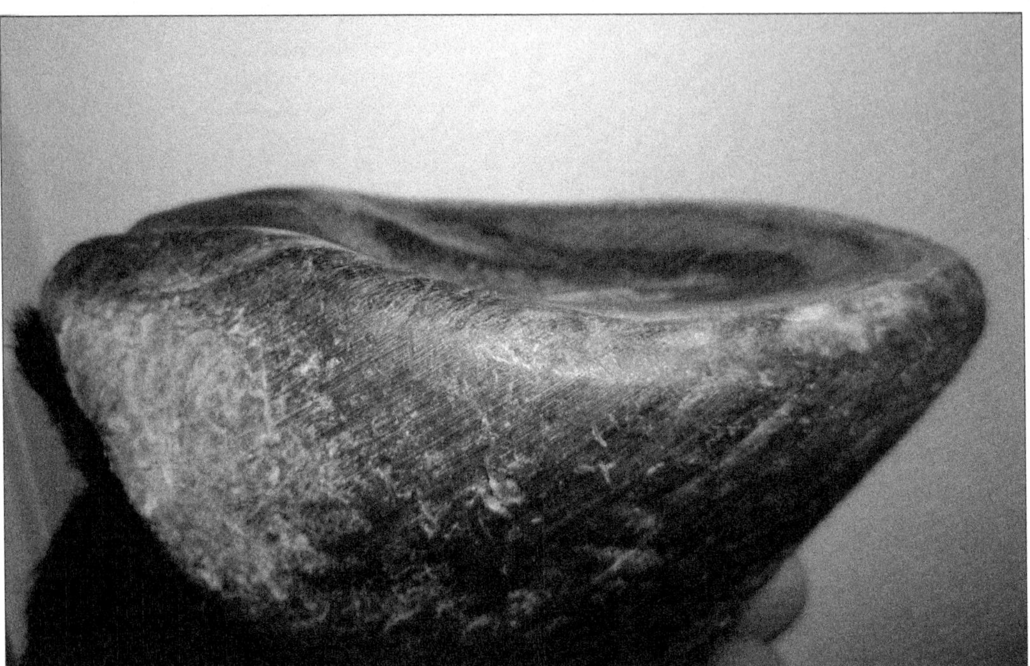

Right front, mediovolar view, wild hoof (U.S Great Basin)

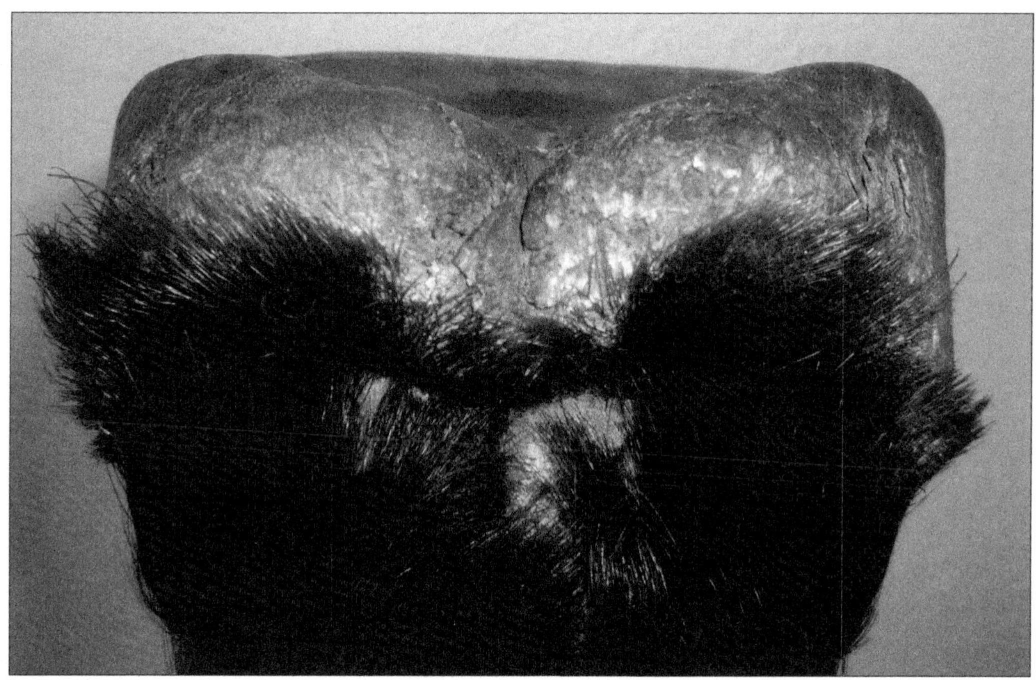

Left hind, posterior view, wild hoof (U.S Great Basin)

Right front, dorsovolar view, wild hoof (U.S Great Basin)

(Continued from page 19)

Study assignments
Naturally shaped hooves in the U.S. Great Basin

Study Assignment #1 – *The Natural Horse: Foundations for Natural Horsemanship.* Jaime Jackson

– This is going to be your first "big read" about our model's hooves – but shy of how to mimic them through trimming. Bear in mind, I wrote this chapter nearly 30 years ago (1988)! Our NHC language has changed considerably since then, but the descriptions of what I saw first hand are as valuable today as they were back then. This is information you need to master, particularly because the 4 *Guiding Principles of the Natural Trim* are based directly on these observations.

- **Chapter 4: "The Natural Horse and Its Hooves"** – This isn't information to glance over lightly, but to study in depth as though the soundness of your own horse was at stake! In fact, the soundness of horses in your care as a practitioner will depend directly on your clear understanding of this material.

Study Assignment #2 – *The Natural Trim: Principles and Practice.* Jaime Jackson

– I wrote Chapter 4 of the previous assignment in 1988. In this assignment (#2) we're going to jump ahead 24 years to 2012 to see how I cover the same material in *The Natural Tim* but with new NHC language and new perspectives on how to look at the wear characteristics we mimic.

- **Chapter 4: "Wear Characteristics of the Naturally Shaped Hoof"** – Once more, read for detail, but also contrast this presentation with the 1988 version above (Assignment #1). Both, coincidentally, ended up in their respective chapter 4, but I didn't plan it that way.

Study Assignment #3 – Power Point Lectures

– More important information that augments Assignments #1 and #2.

- **"Natural Wear Patterns"** – 25 slides also put together in 2014.

Quiz (True or False)
Naturally shaped hooves in the U.S. Great Basin

1. Front hooves tend to be wider and rounder through the toes than hind hooves.
2. Hind hooves tend to grow at lower angles down the toe than front hooves.
3. Jackson found that over 99% of the hooves varied less than 5/8 inches (1.6 cm); and, according to his statistical data curve, nearly 70% varied by less than 3/8 inches (.95 cm).
4. 30% of the hooves Jackson studied had hooves that contained some pigmentation, nearly half of those had no pigmentation.
5. Jackson's study found that the hoof's angle of growth, measured in terms of the visible horn tubules of the outer wall, decreased from toe to heel.
6. Another important finding of Jackson concerned frog pressure. Jackson discovered, as farriers had always contended, that frogs press directly against the ground during the hoof's support phase.
7. Farriers often "set" toe angle by manipulating heel length and/or toe length with respect to each other, but Jackson's data showed that toe angle has no relationship at all to heel or toe lengths.
8. With respect to a hoof's "center line", Jackson found another very peculiar difference between front and hind hooves: front hooves tended to be symmetrical in their bottom and front views, meaning they were divided into two equal left and right sides, whereas hinds tended to be symmetrical in their bottom views but asymmetrical (not evenly divided into left and right sides) in their front views.
9. Jackson interpreted the most protruding support points of the hoof wall as areas of "active wear," where descending weight-bearing forces exerted the greatest pressure on the hoof.
10. Jackson did not believe that areas of "passive wear" resulted from hoof wall being worn away, rather that areas of active wear resulted from a thickening of the hoof wall, which he likened to calluses.

[Answer key is in appendix!]

Research, experimentation, and the birth of NHC Science

Fate would have it that during this same period of time, I was contracted to be the only farrier (I was still a farrier during this stage of my studies) for a large Peruvian Paso breeding operation.[1] This included hundreds of horses of all ages, including many breeding stallions. Most of the horses lived in huge "dry lot" paddocks, free of any grass.[2] *Serendipitously*, the owners wanted everything barefoot – no shoeing. Moreover, only a few of the horses, mainly stallions, were ridden – and ridden barefoot by the Peruvian trainer. At the same time, a few of my other clients were willing to remove the shoes from their horses (most were not willing). In all, I saw a welcomed opportunity to put my wild horse research to the test. Bear in mind, the language and science of NHC that we know and use today did not yet exist – but, intuitively, I knew all that was about to happen. Yet, if I were to point a finger to a time and place where it all began (outside of wild horse country), it was here at the Paso ranch and with my other clients, willing and unwilling to be barefoot.

serendipitous – finding valuable or agreeable things not sought for

At this critical juncture in my research, I had formed an unprecedented *hypothesis*: by simply mimicking the wear patterns of wild horse hooves, the growth patterns of the hooves would shift towards their wild state. But this wasn't exactly novel, because I had earlier stumbled onto the idea as a result of several experiences, which, by now, you've already read about in *The Healing Angle* reading assignment. As I wrote in Chapter 2,

hypothesis – an idea or theory that is not proven but that leads to further study or investigation

> As early as 1982, I began to experiment, blindly, by today's standards of NHC, with what I called the "wild horse trim" . . . What I did at the hoof was remarkably simple. I simply *mimicked* the shape of the wild horse hoof. This seemed like a logical thing to do. But I must confess that the act of mimicking the shape of the wild horse hoof had no more thought given to what the consequences might be than the act itself. Which is to say that importing the shape of the wild horse hoof was simply a mechanical action, and one I recognized that would require repeating, since the hoof continued to grow. In my mind, regrettably, it amounted to little more than the act of trimming the hoof on a regular

[1]Hacienda de la Solana. Guerneville, CA (USA). An interesting note: the ranch's veterinarian, the late and distinguished Dr. John Woolsey, later sent me a letter saying he has never seen so many sound horses in one place in his entire career. Dr. Woolsey, previously an instructor at the University of California, Davis, School of Veterinary Medicine, and appointed to the State's Board of Veterinary Examiners by Gov. Ronald Reagan, retired my last year at the Paso ranch, 1988. He passed away in 2011 at age 88.

[2]Grass pastures are notable as being triggers for Whole Horse Inflammatory Disease (WHID), which you will learn more about later in related study assignments.

> basis before nailing a shoe to it. Not that there's anything wrong with that, because, in fact, that is what we have to do. Only that, I soon discovered, there's more, a lot more to the bigger picture – and the consequences, in particular, of mimicking that wild shape . . . The process might have ended there, except that I begin to notice that, among clients with unshod hooves . . . the hoof's growth patterns began to modulate increasingly towards the Great Basin wild hoof model.

So, that's when the hypothesis actually began to form in my mind. If my observations were correct concerning what I thought was happening, then I must then set about to prove it over time. This simple act, as time revealed, would be the door opener to facilitating naturally shaped hooves. But at the onset, it was clear to me that time and circumstances had come together to enable me to prove, or disprove, this hypothesis. Given the diversity of my clientele, I decided to test the wild horse model along two tracks: *those horses that would go barefoot and those that would remain shod.* Both groups would receive the same trim. Within months, the outcomes were perfectly clear. The barefoot sample yielded healthier, stronger, and more naturally shaped hooves; shod hooves, in stark contrast, remained weaker and more sensitive between setting shoes, and naturally growth patterns were obviously suppressed. The former could walk carefree down a gravel road barefooted without issue, the other was more tentative or simply unable due to hypersensitivity. Shoeing, I concluded, damaged hooves, prevented natural wear patterns from developing, obstructed the natural gaits, and compromised clinical soundness.

I did struggle quite a bit back then to create a new way of understanding the native *morphology* of the horse's foot with an eye to establishing a method, what would become the "natural trim" we know and practice today. There were many unknowns, but I always believed that the A-force I knew existed in the species, would be my greatest ally in the quest to unravel the mysteries of the genuine naturally shaped hoof. The basic natural trim guidelines described in this training manual represent the culmination of 35 years of my findings, experimentation, and unfaltering belief in the ancient adaptation.

morphology – the form and structure of an organism or any of its parts

As I worked to define and refine what we call today the "artful science" of natural hoof care, and the natural trim specifically, I was repeatedly drawn back into wild horse country – far away from the BLM corrals! – to learn more about the wild horses I had come to trust and appreciate as my teachers. These adventures into wild horse country gave birth to the broader science of "natural horse care" and what we know and practice today as the "4 Pillars of NHC". Without these foundational pillars, I had come to realize, the A-force was weakened or obstructed altogether. The natural trim would be deemed irrelevant among processionals and horse owners alike. To me, this outcome was unacceptable, and so I turned my sights above and beyond the hoof to the very lifestyle of the wild horse.

4 Pillars of NHC

The natural trim is one of four "pillars" - the foundational elements - of natural horse care. All four pillars evolved out of my ongoing wild horse research in the U.S. Great Basin (1982—1986). NHC science defines these today as *Paddock Paradise*, a *reasonably natural diet*, *natural horsemanship*, and the *natural trim*. Each pillar is rooted in the lifestyle, and more particularly the behaviors, of the wild horse. And like the natural trim, each pillar is a simulated representation that mimics what has been observed in their natural world. For example, we may ask, what is it that wild horses do to create strong, healthy bodies (and minds) and hooves? The 4 Pillars answer this question. Students of natural hoof care who want the best outcome for their natural trims, must then give attention and study to all four pillars, not just one or another.

This training program provides for this broad learning opportunity — not just hoof trimming. It is astonishing that since the founding of the AANHCP in the year 2000, and the sweeping barefoot hoof care revolution that has reached all continents, that the vast international population of horse owners are either marginally aware of the 4 Pillars, or have never heard of them. This disconnect from our wild horse model is alarming. It is incumbent upon ISNHCP students like yourself to help us change this in the name of humane care of horses. The learning materials provided by this training program will give you the necessary foundational understanding needed to spread the word.

Significantly, these materials have *seminal* value, meaning that to gain from them the most they have to offer, students should reference them often as their understanding of NHC and the natural trim continues to grow. Wisdom speaks to the bottomless well of knowledge imparted by the wild horse model, and it is the wise student who recognizes that the very complexity of nature reveals itself in layers of growing awareness. One layer paves the way for the next. For example, an idea invariably remains an "abstraction" until a skill brings it to life in such a way that it is understood. In the wild, I learned that to understand equine "telos," the

seminal – having a strong influence on ideas, works, events, etc., that come later

nature of the horse, I must learn patience and the willingness to absorb and understand that which I saw, heard, smelled, and touched. In this way, I was able to overcome unsubstantiated opinions, myths, and conventions of domestication that otherwise would plague my ability to see and understand the horse's wild state for what it is. Thus, in the same way that the natural trim will reveal itself to you in "layers of growing awareness," so to the 4 Pillars will enable you to grow and sustain an even keel as you navigate your way through the corrupting forces of domestication in the field as you ply our trade.

Study Assignments
Research, experimentation, birth of NHC Science, and the 4 Pillars of NHC

Your next task is to enter the NHC world of the other 3 Pillars and learn how they integrate with the natural trim. While this is admittedly going to be a fairly substantial undertaking for you, it is also a very interesting and important one. Again, the most successful path one can take in mastering the natural trim in the "real world" of domesticated horses, is the one that includes a well-rounded understanding of how all 4 Pillars work together. This module of independent study is where most students fail – not recognizing the supreme importance of the connection to our wild horse model. By "connecting the dots" to our model at every turn, and with humility and understanding, the entire breadth and depth of natural hoof care will yield to you with great clarity. Although seldom the easiest or shortest path to take, it is the *proven* path to excellence and wisdom, and unequivocally the one that is the most rewarding.

Study Assignment #1 – *The Natural Horse: Foundations for Natural Horsemanship.* (1997 edition) Jaime Jackson

– Before the term "4 Pillars" congealed in my mind in those exact words, I had already come to realize that the natural trim would have to take its position in the context of related "natural horse care" practices. So, we're going to venture back 30 years ago to another time when I first talked about what would become the 4 Pillars we know today, albeit in a slightly different language but with the same meaning and significance.

- **Chapter 3: "Movement of the Natural Horse** – Admittedly, this chapter is not an easy one to work through. Some of the gait analysis is pretty tedious, and I don't expect you to spend a whole lot of time here on this specifically; technically, however, it becomes very important if you are going to ride a horse and not cause harm, or, as part of the Advanced Trim Guidelines (ATG) Training Program, when you will need to be strong on the natural gaits to deduce causality associated with lameness. I also took the liberty for the reason given in the chapter to cross-reference the natural movements of the horse with classical horsemanship, including comments from Xenophon's *Art of Horsemanship (c. 400 BC)*, absolutely worth reading in its own right. Since it's a bit lengthy overall, I would use the illustrations as important reference points to anchor your studies. The more important ones I want you to focus on are the discussions associated with the diagram on page 33, and Tables 3-1 and 3-2.

I should also point out here that some people have said this is actually the most controversial chapter in the book, and that it marks the beginning of the natural horse care movement. Not because of the gait analysis, but because of the inclusion of one short section, "Importance of Habitat," beginning on page 37. I remember to this day when I was about to put pen to paper, thinking, "Oh boy, should I say this?" I'll quote where the controversy starts and let you read the rest in the book: "My advice to horse owners interested in developing the natural horse in their own horses is some rather unconventional changes in barnyard management . . . First, tear down the stalls and fences and let the horses run . . ."

- **Chapter 5: "General Care of the Horse"** – One could argue that the controversial section cited above, and this chapter were the foundations for natural boarding, and for my book, *Paddock Paradise*. Actually, that would be true. In that book, I explain my reasons for the delay in writing it. In fact, the book is one of your reading assignments below, so you'll read about it there! Needless to say, this is another important chapter, if for no other reason, I systematically challenged conventional care practices from boarding, to hoof care, to worming, to riding, to any concept or practice that harmed the horse for whatever reason based on my observations. It is interesting to me that although my book *The Natural Horse* is actually a humanitarian "defense of the horse" based on nature, to the best of my knowledge, neither animal rights organizations nor humane societies have embraced it. Figure that one out!

- **Chapter 7: "A Natural Way to Ride"** – As I say in the opening sentence of this chapter, my intent was to cross-link the "natural state of the horse" with an "approach to horsemanship" that would truly define a "natural rider." I believe this chapter may be where the term "natural horsemanship" originated, although I first introduced it on page 7 of the book's *Introduction*. The term came as an inspiration from my wild horse studies as early as 1982, when I began suggesting it to clients as a riding concept along with the "wild horse trim" (which I abandoned quickly as the word "wild" was too much for clients). It's interesting that Wikipedia cites another text as the original source:

> "Natural horsemanship" is a more recent term, originating in the western United States, and not coming in to popular use until around 1985. Its origin is widely attributed within the movement to Pat Parelli, who wrote a book using the phrase in the title.

Parelli's book, "Natural Horse • Man • Ship" was published in 1993, but had no connection to wild horses. *The Natural Horse* was published in 1992, although I had written the book four years earlier. Parelli himself credits Alois Podhajsky's *Complete Training of Horse and Rider* as foundational to his methods, which I also cite in *The Natural Horse*. I had never met nor heard of Parelli until after his book was published even though he and I worked our separate professions at the same time and place near Castro Valley, CA, in the early to mid-1980s. He is seven years younger than me. Another point of interest, I have heard but not confirmed that Parelli gave his first horsemanship clinic in Southern California at Pierce College in Woodland Hills, CA (San Fernando Valley). Ironically, I also developed a trimming clientele there. Small world! To date, insofar as I know, he has never publicly embraced our wild horse model, including the natural trim. Evidence, to my way of thinking, that his concept of "natural horse•man•ship" and our "natural horsemanship" are "oceans" apart.

- **Epilog: "A New Era of Horsemanship"** – Although only a page long, it remains important to me as a call to change in the horse world based on my many observations of horse abuse, of which many are viewed as "acceptable" by convention although they are truly notorious methods which, in my opinion, shouldn't be applied to any living creature.

Study Assignment #2 – *The Natural Trim: Principles and Practice.* Jaime Jackson

– Once more, we'll move forward in time from when I laid the foundations for the 4 Pillars of NHC in *The Natural Horse*, to the present. Again, not surprisingly, the language has changed, but the concepts have not. As important, today there are living adaptations of those concepts embodied in Paddock Paradise around the world (Assignment #3) and in the safe, reasonably natural diet advocated by the AANHCP and ISNHCP.

- **Chapter 2: "Four Pillars of NHC"** – Once more, read for detail, but also contrast with what I wrote in *The Natural Horse*. "TNT," as I call this book, was written in 2012, so even here, some of the information is dated. For example, we've updated diet information, and you will find the AANHCP recommended diet in the DVD you received along with the PowerPoint lectures and other important information. There are many new innovations in our AANHCP Paddock Paradise, and I've tried to include things we're doing as late as 2016. But get used to this, NHC isn't about standing still. As I always tell our members, "We are not here to hold ground, we are here to move forward."

Study Assignment #3 – *Paddock Paradise: A Guide to Natural Horse Boarding.* Jaime Jackson – Read the entire book. Paddock Paradise is the logical outcome of "General Care of the Horse" in Study Assignment #1 above. Generally considered an "easy read," my approach here is to have you read the entire book from cover to cover, without specific chapter assignments. But this is not to say that because it is a relatively "easy read," that the material isn't of great importance. To the contrary, the concept and content is resonating with horse owners widely across the horse world, in nearly every continent, because they are able to implement changes in their management practices that genuinely help horses based on our wild horse model.

Study Assignment #4 – *Laminitis: An Equine Plague of Unconscionable Proportions.* Jaime Jackson – Read the entire book. Although the focus and training will not include horses stricken by laminitis with deformed hooves, understanding what the disease is, how it occurs, and how to prevent it, is vital to your education. As I explained at the onset of this training manual, and as you will see in this book, special training is required to meet the challenges of laminitis at the hoof (*facing page*).

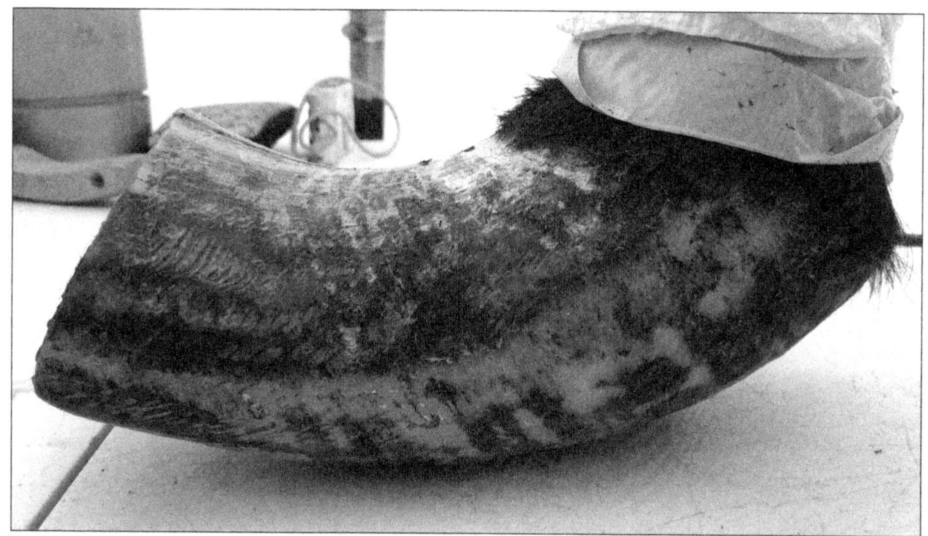

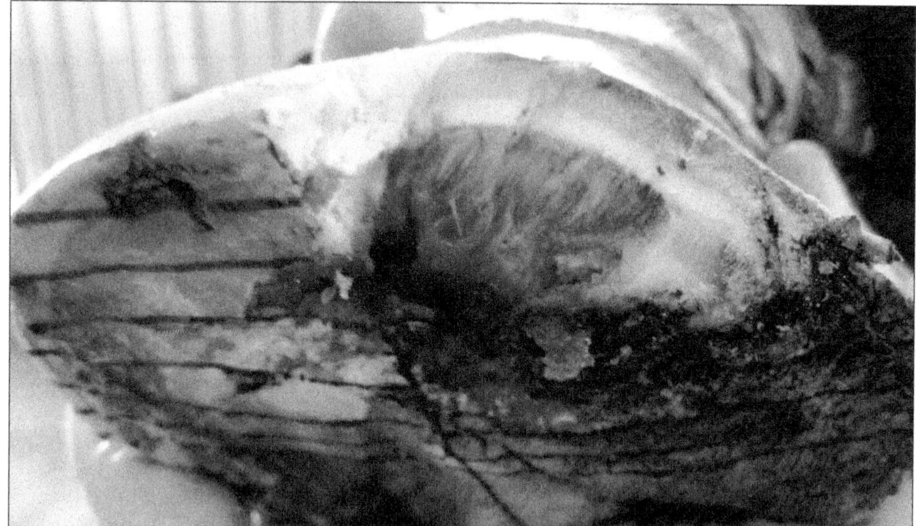

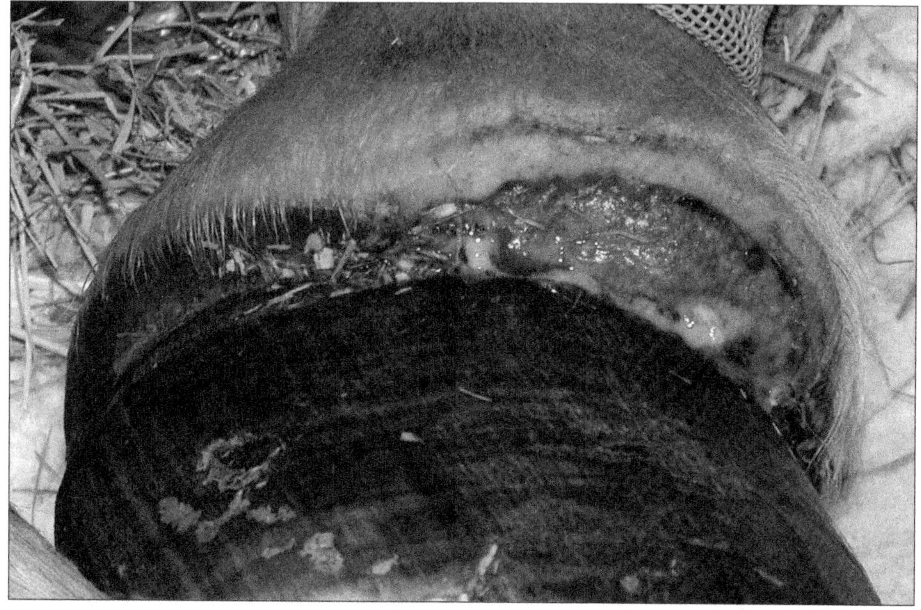

If the basics of the natural trim are not mastered first, trimming hooves with extreme capsule deformity is an invitation to confusion, panic, unnecessary suffering – and even death – for the horse. One must know what they are doing and why, not "wanting to know what to do and why." The ISNHCP offers advanced training for those students who, through their training reports, field and written exams, case studies, and final written reports, demonstrate excellence in the basics.

***PowerPoint Lecture* – "4 Pillars of NHC"** – Another important learning session, which discusses further the *4 Guiding Principles of the Natural Trim* with examples of how they are typically violated.

Quiz (True or False)
Research, experimentation,
NHC Science, and the 4 Pillars of NHC

1. The natural habitat of the wild horse is a passive player in the natural gaits of the horse, whereas behavior is an active force.
2. Horses do not naturally move backwards.
3. Behavior in the horse that is natural, but defiant, will require a "correction" from us to assert our relative dominance, whereas behavior that is malicious signals that the horse is responding from fear to do unreasonable demands having been made upon them, and no correction is warranted.
4. "Feed Stations" in Paddock Paradise are a way to feed horses that mimics grazing/browsing/foraging behavior – eating small amounts of forage throughout the day – and which stimulates horses to move from one place to the next as they do in the wild.
5. It is natural for horses led by a monarch alpha male to move from one place to the next in Paddock Paradise, for example, from one feed station to the next, in order of relative dominance.
6. All stallions are alphas, all geldings are betas.
7. A "reasonably natural diet" is one that meets the nutritional requirements of the horse, is comprised mainly of "safe" mixed-grass hays, and minor quantities of supplements determined to be safe by the AANHCP. It does not cause laminitis.

U.S. Government Archives

As quick as wild horses emerged on the U.S. Great Plains and Great Basin in the late 1600s, and possibly earlier, American Indians became horsed, forming warrior societies that pitted Indian against Indian, and ultimately Indian against the U.S. Government, leading to the end of an unprecedented horse culture based on our model.

8. WHID is another word for laminitis.

9. The three stages of laminitis are *sub-clinical* (symptoms with the absence of pain), *clinical* (symptoms accompanied by pain), and *chronic* (symptoms that are both *clinical* and *sub-clinical*).

10. Vets have no role in the treatment of laminitis.

[Answer key is in appendix!]

Natural Trim Defined

This brings us back to the very definition of the "natural trim" stated in this training manual's introduction, which, like the AANHCP-ISNHCP vital mission, should be committed to memory or in one's own words that convey the same meaning. Reduced simply to what we do, the natural trim is defined as *mimicking in the natural wear patterns of the wild horse hoof.*

In this interpretation, the natural trim is simply a mechanical process of manipulating hoof mass. Of course, how and exactly where this mass is manipulated is arguably easier said than done, which is why we have a training program! But, this simple definition is the correct one because, in fact, that is all that we do at the hoof. All of us began here at this most elementary level, learning how to master the basic trim method that years of experience have taught us how to best achieve the sought natural wear patterns. Once mastered, the deeper layers of complexity due to the hoof's response will be revealed to you. Advanced training awaits the accomplished student who wishes to pursue the A-force in the battles against pathology, the mysteries of nature's healing powers, and new research.

Study Assignments
The Natural Trim Defined

This is another area of study that will add to your depth of understanding of where the natural trim came from. To be clear, what follows is not intended as trimming instructions, although instructions do appear in the first assignment. Your journey here begins back again in the 1980s when I wrote the trimming guidelines in *The Natural Horse*. We don't use them in that form today for several reasons.

First, they were written for farriers, like myself back then, who would use them for shoeing purposes, and for those interested, as a barefoot method. The latter was very controversial in those early days, and my closest advisors in the industry implored me to say nothing about de-shoeing horses. I did it anyways, as you've read in an earlier assignment, but I also tucked it away under the heading "Riding Unshod Horses" in the hoof care chapter in the first assignment below, hoping not to alienate fellow farriers but to quietly invite the more open-minded ones to the possibility of de-shoeing. Of course, I risked the hostility of the horseshoe manufacturers and their affiliates (nails, pads, forges, shoeing tools, etc.). In the end, this was the case, and the wild horse model was rejected — fueled by politics and ignorance.

Not everyone in the industry turned their back on it, however, and your readings in *The Natural Trim* (book's) introduction testify to this. It is a credit to the American Farriers Association that they also welcomed my articles in their journal spanning a decade, and even invited me to speak at their annual conference in 1988, where the model was put before 5,000 attending farriers. Veterinary organizations also invited me to speak at their events, which I did. Had none of these opportunities occurred, it is very likely you and I would not be here together right now in this training manual. Still, farriers and vets in the field have not risen to the occasion and continue with their trades pretty much unchanged. Indeed, the farrier still approaches the hoof as a "dead" subject and attention is given exclusively to how steel can be shaped to effect gait, not the health and vitality of the foot, which is given such minor lip service as to border on criminal malpractice. This shortsightedness, reinforced by the veterinary community's self-imposed ignorance of the horse's natural state, reflects the farrier industry's lack of any attention to or interest in the biology of the hoof. Such neglect bears direct responsibility for the great harm shoeing, past and present, has caused the horse and his feet. Obviously, such behavior is a blatant violation of our vital mission.

The second reason we don't use those earlier instructions is that we have much better ones today to follow. Bear in mind as you venture through each of these study assignments, the natural trim *method* is itself continuously given to changes that reflect our constantly improving understanding of its impact on the living foot. What we know in the present is what you will be taught. The politics, influence, and restraints of the farriery sciences have since been shed, and the methodology of the natural trim has been free to evolve in its own right. We know much more today about how it works then I did back then. We continue to grow. And if anyone thinks it will be the same 10 years from now, they will probably be sadly disappointed!

Study Assignment #1 – *The Natural Horse: Foundations for Natural Horsemanship.* (1997 edition) Jaime Jackson

– Read these instructions for their historical perspective as explained above. I want students to know our roots, what it was like at the beginning, and that things are done much differently today. This is not say our earliest instructions aren't important, only that they are limited by today's standards and precision guidelines.

Our manner of measuring the hooves, for example, has improved, as has our understanding of how and what tools should be deployed. We use new tools and equipment today that didn't exist then. These came about because our insights and understanding of what was needed to affect hoof mass in the most precise and effective way necessitated them. Like the trim method, the co-evolution of NHC tools/equipment is a huge story in and of itself.

- **Chapter 6: "Hoof Care the Natural Way"**– Notice that the guidelines are directed at "experienced farriers," and that much of the detail that goes into today's natural trim guidelines are for the most part missing. The reason for this is that I presumed basic tool handling skills were possessed by the professional farrier, and that they would know how to measure, and could also interpret and apply the data curve in *Figure* 6-2 to the trimming steps described. I understood that in all likelihood, whatever they did would probably be covered with a nailed-on horseshoe. Unless, I calculated, they "took the bait" and went for the section, "Riding an Unshod Horse," which concluded with a message to the horse owner, "refrain from riding any unshod horse unless you have the close cooperation of a knowledgeable and open-minded shoer." But then, I went ahead anyway and gave the owner-reader advice on what to do to go barefoot – which I had sounded out with the Peruvian trainer at the breeding operation I talked about earlier in this training manual. My decision to include this information was considered treasonous by sectors of the farrier community. I consider the final two sections of the book dealing with abuse and lameness to be the benchmark of "animal rights for equines" based on the natural state of the horse, and which is implicit in our vital mission today nearly 30 years later.

Study Assignment #2 – *The Natural Trim: Principles and Practice.* Jaime Jackson

– This and the PowerPoint assignment that immediately follows will be the last discussions of what defines the natural trim before we enter the stepwise methodology itself that we use today.

- **Chapter 5: "The Natural Trim Defined"** – This is not a long chapter but an important one for two reasons: it defines the limits of the natural trim; and explains the trim's place in the holistic picture of natural horse care. It goes without saying, this is also important information for horse owners because it also explains their role in our world of NHC relative to the natural trim. Written in 2012.

Study Assignment #3 – Power Point Lectures: "Foundational Principles of the Natural Trim" – 34 slides put together in 2016, so very recent information. Echoes information in Assignment #2.

Quiz Assignment

The Natural Trim Defined

Rather than give you a T/F quiz, here's what I want you to do: ask a horse owner friend or a captive family member to listen to your explanation of what a natural trim for a horse is, including its limits, and what their responsibilities are as the horse's owner. Explain to them the 4 Pillars of NHC. After this, interview them to see how well they understood you. Write down questions for them to answer. Afterwards, evaluate the results, asking yourself, and them, how well you communicated what NHC is all about. Ask them what you could do to improve your communication of this information. Ask them if you can interview them again after you've completed all your training. Keep your notes and compare them. I might ask you to write a paper on this for your written report leading to full ISNHCP Practitioner status!

Step 1 – ISNHCP Training Program

Independent Study

Part 2 - Structures of the Horse's Foot

Students of the natural trim must have a basic knowledge of the outer and internal structures of the horse's foot. The outer parts are most important because we will be impacting them directly with our trimming. To a lesser extent, there must be an understanding of the inner structures that are responsible for creating and maintaining the outer structures we can see and touch. Penetrating these internal structures with our tools can cause serious harm to the foot. Part 3 of this training manual identifies both inner and outer structures that we are concerned with as trimmers. It explains their locations, what their purposes are, and which ones specifically we are going to trim.

An important distinction should be made between the oft heard terms "hoof, capsule, and foot." Hoof and capsule are synonymous, and describe the outer part of the horse's foot we can see and touch. The learning materials use both terms, even though they mean the same thing. You will run into both in the hoof care world, too!

"Foot," in contrast, refers to all of the parts of the horse's foot including both outer and inner structures. The parts of the horse's foot include the hoof (outer part), bones, tendons and ligaments, joints, nerves, blood vessels, and fibro-fatty (cushioning) structures. The foot is also referred to as an "organ," because it is a specialized part of the body (like the heart, liver, and stomach) that performs a specific function.

This is not a comprehensive anatomy and physiology course on the horse's foot, nor does it have to be in order for you to become a solid basic natural trim professional. At this level of training, students only need to know how to trim the hooves according to the basic natural trim guidelines. A deeper knowledge of the horse's foot really only comes into play when tackling the problems associated with upper body trauma, diseases of the foot, and extreme capsule deformity. This represents advanced training, however, that is only available to students who successfully complete this training program and can meet the entrance requirements to the ISNHCP *Advanced Natural Trim Training Program* discussed later in this training manual.

In the following discussions, you'll be facing new terminology that describes the horse's foot. We all have to learn these. Fortunately, there's not that many to learn. Here's how I want you to tackle them: read – but don't study (yet) – the next five sections. They're not very long. With a marker, underline or mark the anatomical terms you don't really know anything about. To help, I've italicized the ones I really want you to focus on and mark. That will bring you to the study assignments. I'll meet you there for the next directive.

Epidermal structures of the horse's foot

Epidermal structures, also called the epidermis, comprise the outer "skin" of the horse's foot. Together, all the epidermal structures of the foot are referred to as the *hoof* (or *capsule*). These structures lack nerves and blood supply, however, they are manufactured (created), regulated, and maintained by their internal or *dermal* counterparts within the foot. Because these are the structures directly affected by the natural trim, they will receive the most attention throughout the course of this training program.

Dermal structures

Dermal structures are those inner parts of the foot that manufacture ("create") and maintain ("nourish") the hoof. These dermal structures go by other names, including *dermis* and *corium*. Each *epidermal* structure has its own *dermal* counterpart, thus, we distinguish the *hoof wall corium* from the *sole corium*, the *frog corium*, and so forth. NHC science treats all the foot's coria as a single, integrated body called the *Supercorium*.

The dermal structures are separated from their epidermal structures by another structure called the *basement membrane*, from which new epidermal growth emerges (grows out or off of). These and other nearby structures (e.g., connective tissue) are extremely complex, and the closer one looks at them, the more complex it all gets. In this course, we'll take a more "distant" look!

Bones and joints of the foot

The bones of the horse's foot include the *cannon bone*, *long* and *short pastern bones*, *coffin bone*, and the *navicular bone*. The joints of the foot are formed by the union of these bones. For example, the cannon bone and long pastern bone unite to form the *fetlock joint*, well known to most horse owners. This joint corresponds to the human "ankle." While there is considerable emphasis placed on the alignment of these bones among farriers, vets, and even "generic" (don't follow the wild horse model) barefoot trimmers, this is of little or no interest to the NHC practitioner who simply trims the hoof. The basic natural trim guidelines provide for the natural orientation of these bones. In fact, attempts to manipulate this orientation of the bones with the intent of forcing a particular stance so as to alter the horse's natural gaits, is considered inhumane and constitutes a violation of natural trim guidelines.

Major tendons of the foot

There are two major tendons of the horse's foot, the *deep digital flexor tendon* (DDFT) and the *common digital extensor tendon* (CDET). Like the preoccupation shown by farriers and others concerning orientation of the bones of the foot, we find the same unnecessary and inhumane interventions occurring with these tendons. This is particularly the case with the DDFT, where surgical *tenotomy* is commonly performed to minimize its impact on the coffin bone, to which it is naturally attached for the purpose of flexing the joints of the foot during its flight phase. NHC science rejects this and other interventions that compromise the natural state and function of the tendons. Once more, holistic prevention and intervention measures are followed based on all four of the NHC pillars.

tenotomy – surgical division of a tendon

Other internal structures of the horse's foot

The equine foot is an extremely complex organ with a maze of many moving parts that contribute to its form and function. These include the *vascular* (fluids) network that delivers vital nutrients for healthy hoof growth and overall structure, *nerves* that serve hoof function and optimal *directed growth*, and many other structures such as the *digital cushion* and *cartilages* that serve allied roles. All of these and other structures within the foot and throughout the horse's body do as nature intended when the 4 Pillars of NHC are embraced and implemented by horse owners. Tragically, widespread obsession with pathology and ignorance of NHC science and methods, and has resulted in many veterinary and farriery interventions – including surgery, drugs, and corrective shoeing – that disrupt and degrade the form and function of these structures. Some are so serious as to cause permanent damage and even cause death. ISNHCP students can best serve the horse by mastering the basic natural trim and encouraging horse owners to embrace all four of the NHC pillars.

Study Assignments
Structures of the Horse's Foot

I've given you a brief overview of the major structures comprising the horse's foot. Once again, we're going to go very "light" on the anatomy — no more than what you need to know in order to conduct the natural trim according to our guidelines. So, to help you learn what and where they are located, go ahead and study the materials in the study assignments below. Once you've familiarized yourself with them, return to the previous descriptions and also the next and final section of Part 2 (**"Objectives of the natural trim relative to the dermal and epidermal structures"**) below, where you can test what you learned. If you can't follow what I'm saying in any of these discussions, that simply means you need to go back to these study assignments and look a little closer. In fact, going "back and forth" between them and the training manual is how a lot of this happens in order to reach an understanding. So don't feel alone if you find yourself doing this in order to figure things out. Everyone else is probably doing the same thing! The following quiz should help too. Moreover, as we move into the forthcoming sections and steps on measuring and trimming, we will use them again and again.

Study Assignment #1 — *The Natural Trim: Principles and Practice.* Jaime Jackson

- **Chapter 3: "Major Structures of the Horse's Foot"** — This takes you right into the "meat and potatoes" of the foot's structures. Your goal is to learn their names and locations.

Study Assignment #2 — Power Point Lecture: "Major Structures of the Horse's Foot" — 106 slides. Covers everything in the previous assignment but with more detail and some additional dermal structures.

Quiz (True or False)
Major Structures of the Horse's Foot

1. Each hoof has two bars.
2. The white line lies between the sole and the water line.
3. The "wings" refer to the poster processes of P3.
4. The role of the DDFT is to flex the joints of the foot for flight.
5. The hoof wall is composed of minute hairs that are "glued" tightly together.
6. Horn tubules have semi-hollow cores called medulla.
7. All the epidermal structures are "extruded' by minute *papilla* in the *Supercorium.*
8. The dermal leaves of the lamellar corium are separated by epidermal leaves.
9. The heel bulbs are extensions of the frog.
10. The terminal arch is a vascular structure that connects the digital arteries within the coffin bone.

Objectives of the natural trim relative to the dermal & epidermal structures

There are three *strategically* and holistically integrated *tactical* objectives of the natural trim relative to the dermal and epidermal structures:

strategic – of great importance within an integrated whole or to a planned effect

tactical – of or relating to small-scale actions serving a larger purpose

1. **First, to locate the natural epidermal barriers that protect the dermal beds.**

   We recall from Chapter 4 in *The Natural Trim*, the naturally shaped sole possesses both distinct "live sole" and "hard sole" planes. The *live sole plane* is the outermost part of the sole dermis that possesses nerves and a blood supply (**Figure P2-1**). The *hard sole plane* is the outermost ("visible") part of the epidermal sole. The natural barrier not to be penetrated by thc natural trim is the epidermis lying between these two planes. My research of wild horse hooves, and comparative studies of domesticated hooves, has shown the natural sole thickness of this barrier for the *hard sole plane* to be approximately 1 cm (a little less than one half inch). Coincidentally, and perhaps not surprisingly, this is the same thickness of the average horseshoe! Moreover, my research has shown that this 1 cm epidermal barrier thickness is essentially the same thickness for the naturally shaped hoof wall and frog.

2. **Second, to contour the epidermal barriers so that they mimic natural wear patterns.**

   This is a critically important step of the natural trim because these contours not only facilitate the natural support and flight functions of the hoof, they fa-

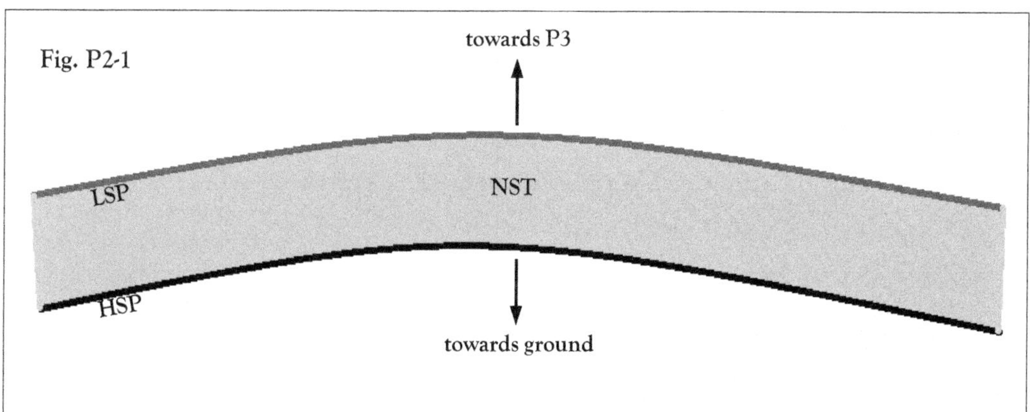

Figure Part 2–1. *Red line* marks the *sole corium*. LSP is the *live sole plane*, which defines the interface between the *sole corium* and new growth forming the epidermal sole. *Black line* marks the *hard sole plane* (HSP), which is the ground facing surface of the naturally shaped sole. *Gray zone* marks the *natural sole thickness* (NST) of the sole, lying between and defined by the HSP and LSP. The NST of the naturally shaped sole is approximately 1 cm (~.4 in).

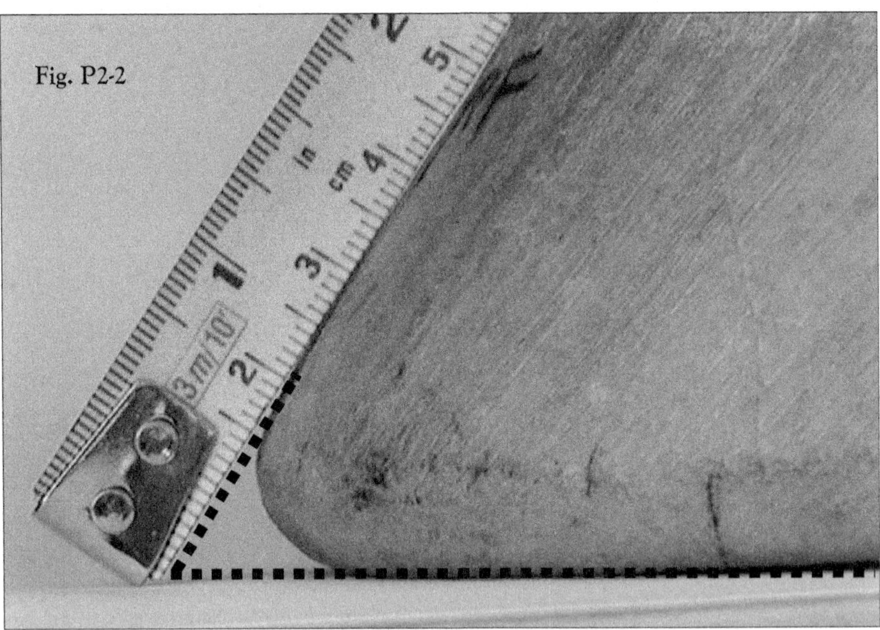

Fig. P2-2. The *mustang roll* is the natural contour of the hoof wall where it meets the ground. The area of wall missing between the two dashed lines is what we remove and mimic with our tools to simulate (if not formed) the mustang roll.

cilitate the optimal transmission of impact forces to and from the dermal and epidermal structures such that they stimulate natural growth patterns (**Figure P2-2**).

3. **And third, to deploy specialized tools in such a way as to enhance the epidermal channels of communication leading from the ground to the vast nerve beds of the Supercorium.**

We have seen in the study assignments that each epidermal structure of the hoof is comprised of a network of specialized hair-like fibers called *tubular horn*. These fibers have a semi-hollow core, called a *medullae*. Each fiber is born of a dermal parent, called a *papillae*. Which is to say, the fibers are growing continuously towards the ground. They are "cemented" together with *intertubular horn* to form the hoof wall. Impact forces — also called concussional forces — pass through the medullae of each fiber, reaching the vast papillary nerve bed of the Supercorium. These forces are countered by weight bearing forces coming from above. Collectively, this "information" is transmitted throughout the horse's entire peripheral nervous system where it is interpreted and redirected in the form of epidermal growth responses. The horse also consciously contributes to these responses through the central nervous system by adjusting foot placement to sustain his locomotive balance.

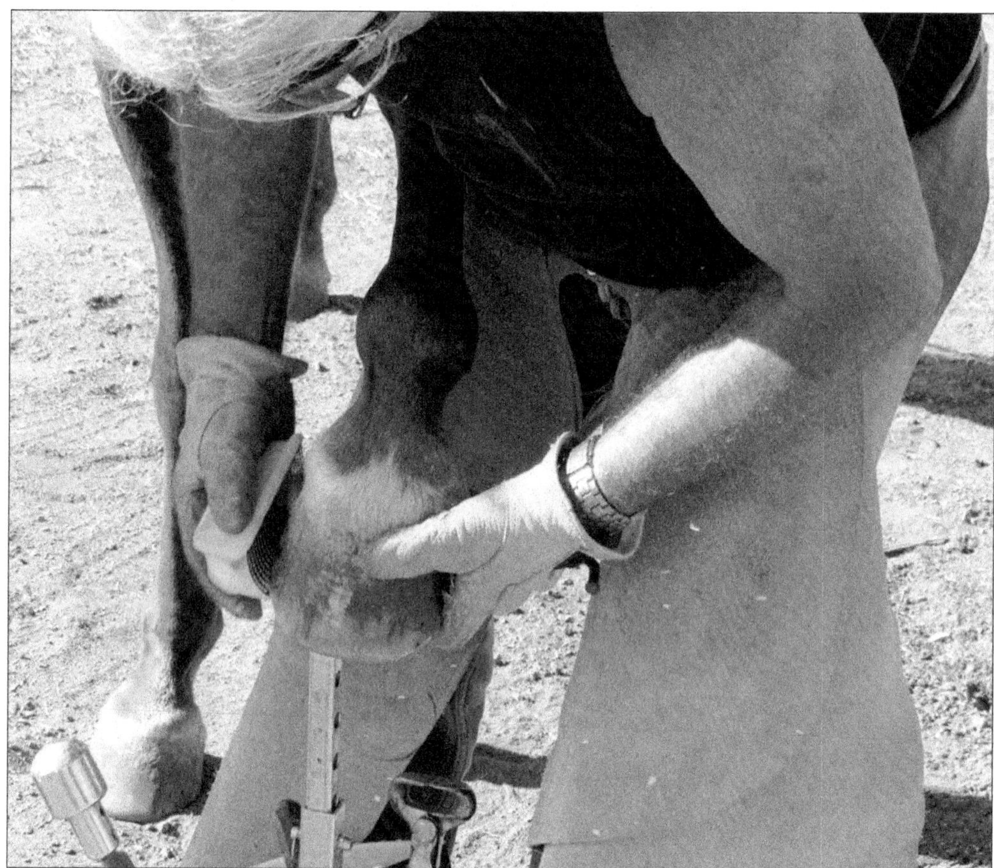

Fig. P2-3. I am "fine-finishing" the *mustang roll* with a radius rasp (RR-1), an innovative hand tool developed specifically for NHC.

Over time, I studied the effects of different tools on the terminal epidermal fibers and the resulting growth responses. I found that "finer" cuts [e.g., with the hoof nipper or Radius Rasp-1 (**Figure P2-3**)] resulted in more natural outcomes than "rough" cuts (e.g., done with the flat rasp). I also recognized that horseshoes obstructed both natural wear and natural growth patterns. A new generation of tools and equipment coincidentally evolved in parallel to the new understanding of natural growth dynamics.

This training program uses dissections of hoof cadavers to help you determine both the natural thickness of the epidermal barriers for each epidermal structure (hoof wall, sole, and frog) as well as the visible shape characteristics (contours) of each epidermal structure's "hard plane." It goes without saying, whether purposefully, or from incompetence, invading this natural barrier of the horse's foot is for humanitarian reasons alone defined as a violation of natural trim guidelines.

Step 1 – ISNHCP Training Program

Independent Study Module

Part 3 – Importance of Measuring

This is an extremely critical part of your studies. In fact, some of my closest colleagues hold that this is *the most important part of one's training in natural hoof care*. I'm one of those who believes this.

My wild horse hoof research focused on specific measurements that would be useful for hoof care professionals in cross-comparing relative naturalness of domesticated hooves. But to gather this data accurately, and in such a way that other professionals could do the same to cross-reference their client horses, I also had to come up with a standard for measuring hooves. Born of this effort are the *Navigational Landmarks* and *Critical Measurements*, a systematic method that enables hoof care professionals to "map out" hooves so they can be measured accurately at the same locations, and then compared to the wild horse hoof data. This necessitated my inventing the *Hoof Meter Reader* (HMR), an unprecedented tool for measuring toe angles and toe lengths of both wild and domesticated hooves (**Figure P3-1**). I've been asked more than once how this invention came about and *why*; here's what I wrote some time ago for earlier ISNHCP students:

> The dilemma goes back to 1982 at the BLM corrals when I first attempted to measure wild horse hooves using a farrier's angle gauge. The gauge is set to the bottom of a flat hoof prepared for shoeing – that's the way we did things back then. But even by then I was already complaining to others that farrier gauges only measured how we trimmed the hoof, and nothing more. So any angle we measured was a reflection of "us," how we trimmed the hoof, but not how nature might shape it. When I tried putting my farrier's gauge on the first wild horse hoof, my suspicions came true. The first week at Litchfield was a complete wash out. The gauge failed to fit the many hoof sizes. Worse, none of the hooves were "flat." It was impossible to even lay the gauge on the convoluted surfaces of the hoof wall. I retreated to my motel room, where I began to construct the first HMR out of pieces of cardboard (later plastic). I set the early HMR against a small flat board with a handle and tried that, and it worked – the truth of "nature" began to reveal itself. The board enabled me to measure angle and length based on how the bottom of a wild horse hoof would stand on a level surface. This worked perfectly for client horses, too.

What evolved out of this HMR experience are two reference planes that you

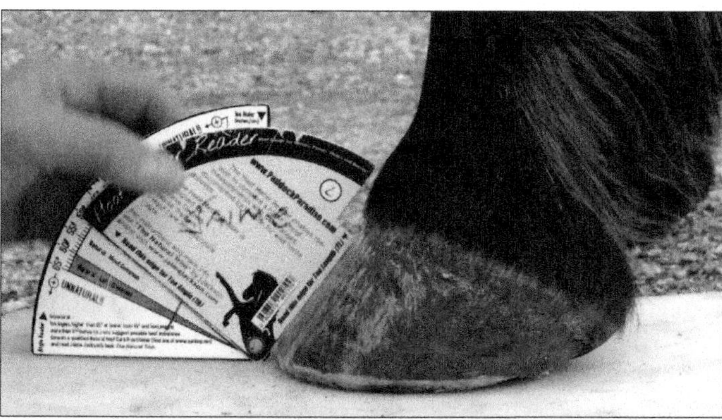

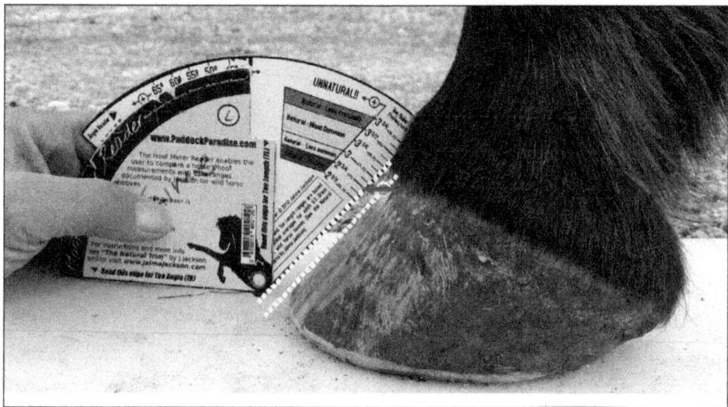

Figure P3-1. Hoof Meter Reader. (*Above*) HMR set to measure toe angle. (*Below*) Set to measure toe length. I'm measuring these hooves on a flat supporting surface (a thick, plastic kitchen cutting board).

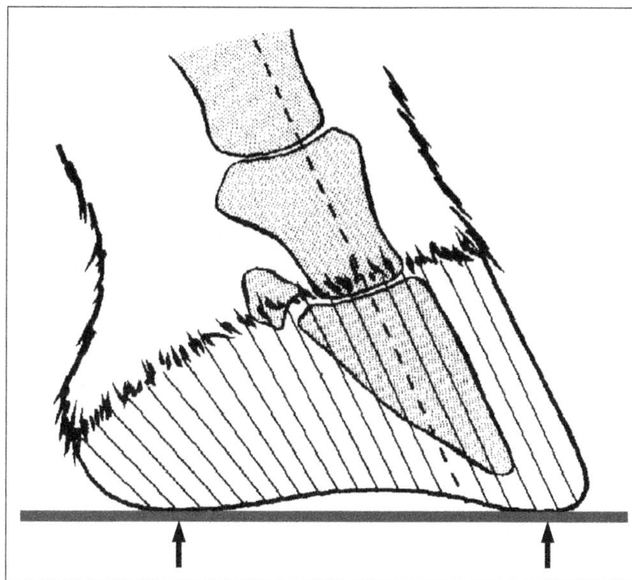

Figure P3-2. Blue line marks the hoof's *Support Plane* (SP). This SP corresponds to the cutting board I'm using in **Figure P3-1**. Arrows point to segments of hoof wall supported by the SP. These points form a single plane called the *Volar Plane*. Hence, the VP equates to and is supported by the SP. The points are also called *active wear*; segments of the hoof wall between active wear are called *passive wear*. How a hoof's VP aligns with the SP defines whether or not a hoof is naturally balanced.

will use every time you measure hooves, both in your **Cadaver Trim Clinic**, and later in the field with live horses. These are the *Support Plane* (SP), which is any level surface that can support the horse's hoof; and the *Volar Plane* (VP), which corresponds to the points of the hoof wall pressing against the SP (**Figure P3-2**). I also discovered that the relationship between VP and SP actually defined "hoof balance." You'll find these simple to use and helpful in learning the natural trim.

Navigational Landmarks

The *Navigational Landmarks* are very specific lines drawn on the hoof relative to certain structures that are common to all equine hooves. Specifically, they form a *grid*, called the *Hoof Plexus* (**Figure P3-3**), a complex network of horizontal and perpendicular lines, planes, and points that facilitate the measuring of hoof "lengths" and "angles" – data that is crucial to trimming to NHC standards based on the wild horse model. It was necessary for me to create the *Hoof Plexus* as a type of geometrical "proof" that explains the relationships between the parts of any equine hoof, wild or domestic: as a means for comparative studies of wild and domestic hooves; as a useful template for tracking mass changes as hooves become more or less naturally shaped under the influence of domestication; and, as a way to navigate extreme capsule deformity associated with *deep pathology*. All of these are important in the broader scheme of NHC. But for your purposes as a beginning student, you will only be concerned with those *Navigational Landmarks* pertinent to the basic natural trim. The good news is that you will find them easy and helpful to use both as a student and a seasoned practitioner in the field.

deep pathology – diseases or trauma that result in severe deformity of the hoof

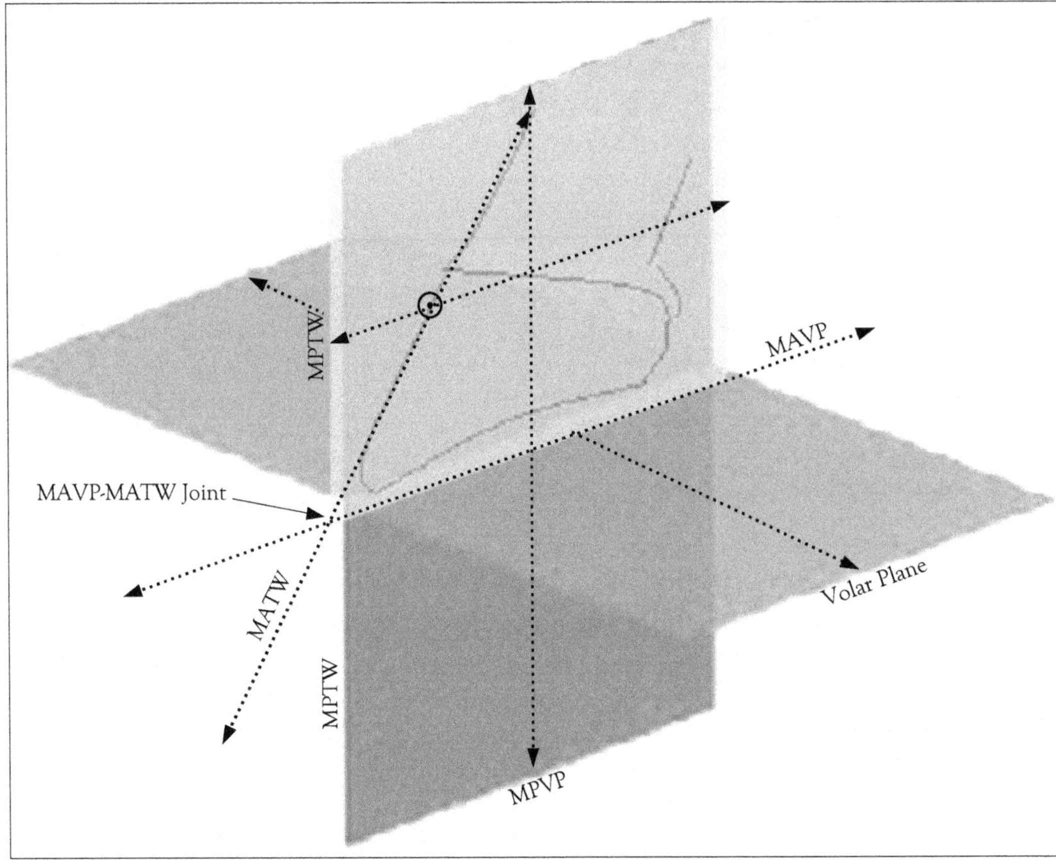

Figure P3-3. Jackson's "Hoof Plexus."

Critical Measurements

The *Navigational Landmarks* enable you to accurately locate and measure what are called the *Critical Measurements*. These include very specific measurements for *toe angle* and *toe length*. There are measurements for other dimensions of the hoof, but those are only relevant to the Advanced Trim Guidelines dealing with deep pathology, or other applications than the trim (e.g., fitting hoof boots).

One may ask: why are the *Critical Measurements* so important, what do they mean exactly, and how do I use them during the natural trim? One of the things I discovered during the course of my research was that horses living in domestication typically generated average measurement data that deviated from the norms established by wild horses I measured. This, I determined, was the result of lifestyle differences. Nevertheless, recognizing that both wild and domesticated horses were still the same species, the data proved to be useful to determine relative naturalness among domesticated horses. As horses were trimmed more naturally, and were also afforded other lifestyle changes in keeping with the 4 Pillars of NHC, I learned that the measurement data became more and more natural relative to data norms I established for wild horses. Conversely, I found that care which violated the 4 Pillars, including how the horses were trimmed, yielded measurement data that became less and less natural. These trends were so dramatic that I realized what was needed was a way to characterize both *measurements* and *trends* in ways that could be readily interpreted by trimmers working with domesticated horses.

To differentiate "wild" versus "domestic" data – in view of their contrasting norms – I classified all wild horse data as "natural" and all domestic data as "healing." The term "healing" reflected my observation that when horses are afforded more natural care, measurement data shifted towards being more natural. In other words, the data "migration" towards naturalness reflected the A-force's healing impact on the horse. Thus, emerging directly from the measurement data came a new NHC language that gave new meaning to terms like "angle" and "length." NHC practitioners could now cross-reference any given hoof to its relative wild state and also evaluate healing changes occurring due to lifestyle changes. Very exciting!

The *Critical* Measurements we are concerned with in learning the basic natural trim guidelines concern *toe length* and *toe angle*. Specifically, these are the *Healing Toe Angle*, or "H°," and the *Healing Toe Length*, or "H°TL." Their "wild" counterparts are *Natural Toe Angle*, or "N°," and *Natural Toe Length*, or "N°TL." Again, H° and H°TL apply only to domesticated horses, whereas N° and N°TL apply only to wild, free-roaming horses of the U.S. Great Basin (their species's adaptive environment[1]).

H° and H°TL

So, insofar as your trimming goes, both as student and in the field as a professional, you will be dealing mainly with H° and H°TL. There are two other closely relate measurements you will need to know how to take too, but we'll get to those in a minute. Right now, let's look at a simplified example of measuring H° and H° TL.

Using the same hooves featured in **Figure P3-1** a few pages back, let's look closer at how these *Critical Measurements* were taken with the *Hoof Meter Reader* (HMR). By now, you should have your own HMR, so bring it out and follow along with my example – it's time to start familiarizing yourself with it. I've enlarged both photos (**Figure P3-4** and **Figure P3-5**) enough that you can read the measurements and compare them on your HMR. Let's read them together. On the top photo, the *yellow dial* of the HMR is pressed flat against the toe wall; the *white dial* lies flat on the *SP* (remember that term?!). I've added the *white arrow* to the photo, which points to the angle reader on the HMR. It reads H° = 51 degrees" (51°). Now, find 51° on your HMR's *Angle Reader*. Not hard, eh? Of course, we did this without using the Navigational Landmarks that would have guided us to exactly where I put the HMR on the toe wall. Don't worry, we'll get to those later. They make it even easier to use the HMR! By the way, by now you've probably noticed that there are different colors on the HMR sides – these correspond to left and right hooves; otherwise, they measure exactly the same. Last, notice the natural scale below the angle read out: it says the angle is "Natural – Most Common." If you rotate the yellow dial out of the way, you can see how the entire scale reads for other angle measurements. This is your direct connection to wild horse country.

Moving to the lower photograph, now the *yellow dial* is on the SP, and the *white dial* is placed parallel to the toe wall, but not directly against it. I've added the *yellow dashed lines* to show what I mean by parallel. It's set apart from the wall because the hair and skin above the hoof is in the way. That's okay, when this happens, just set the HMR away from the hoof enough to make the measurement. The *blue arrow*

[1]This would apply also to comparable biomes in other parts of the world that also suit the adaptation of *E. ferus caballus*.

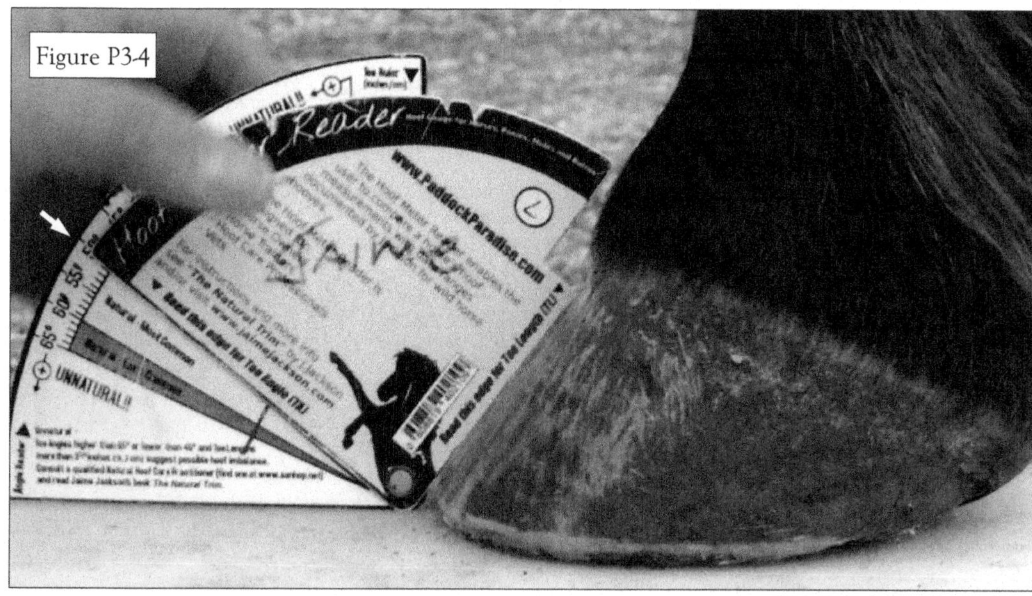

Figure P3-4

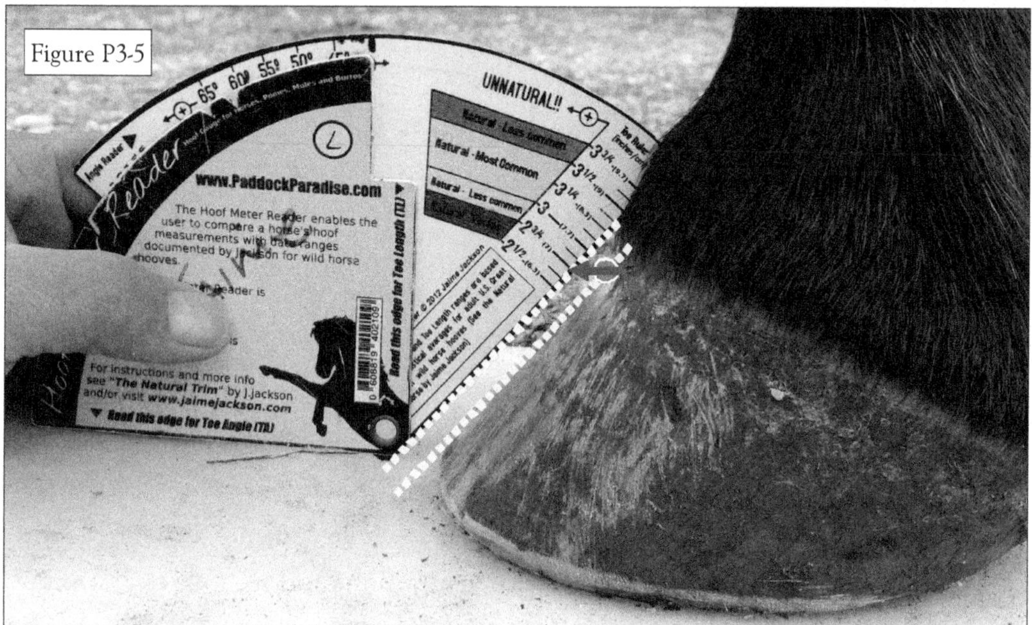

Figure P3-5

points straight across from a Navigational Landmark not visible in the photo. Don't worry about that now, we'll get to it later. For now, just read straight across from the hoof to the white dial. The blue arrow points to H°TL = 2¾ inches (~7 cm). Now, find it on your HMR's *Toe Ruler.*

Using the HMR accurately and efficiently will require some practice. But the effort will be worth it. Your clinicians will be working closely with you to make sure you're using it correctly. But, in the meantime, trying using it on your own horse. Okay, I mentioned two other measurements. Let's go to those now.

B° and B°TL

There are two other measurements, B° and B°TL, that you will need to deal with at least part of the time. These measurements arose in NHC science and practice as a result of chronic hoof deformity, primarily due to *laminitis* (i.e., WHID), violent forms of horsemanship that traumatically breakdown the horse's musculoskelature resulting in *Navicular Syndrome* (NS), and unnatural hoof care practices. I provided examples of each in an earlier reading assignment, *Laminitis: A Plague*.

B° and B°TL are pathological corruptions of H° and H°TL. For example, if the hoof deforms due to laminitis, the toe wall's angle of growth (H°) will corrupt. What happens in life is that the toe wall begins to grow forward and down at a lower angle than at its natural position relative to H°. The lower angle is called B°. Since, by definition, B° is always measured lower on the toe wall than where we measure H°, it gets its name "basement angle." Due to this pathological shift in angle of growth, H°TL (the length of the toe wall relative to the SP) also corrupts to form B°TL. B°TL may measure longer or shorter than H°TL relative to the SP, depending on a number of factors, including neglect, trimming/shoeing methods, surgical interventions, and diet. Now let's try to make sense of all of this using some images of hooves and a couple of new symbols.

Figure P3-6 depicts H° and H°TL for a naturally shaped hoof (it's actually a wild horse hoof, thus, technically N° and N°TL). SP marks the *support plane*. "⊙" is called the bull's-eye (because that's what it looks like), and represents a point on the toe wall we use in measuring toe length. I'll explain later where this point lies exactly, but for now it's simply a way to measure toe length down to the SP. The *blue dashed line* represents H°TL. H°TL is measured down the toe wall from ⊙ to the SP. H° represents the angle at which the toe wall (thus, H°TL) is growing down. Take a few minutes if need be to confirm your understanding. Okay, got that? Now let's move to the laminitic hoof in **Figure P3-7**.

Here, the toe wall (H°TL) suddenly bends and changes direction at the black triangle (▶ = defined as a "diverging toe angle" or *DTA*). At this DTA, H°TL corrupts and becomes B°TL forming the new angle B° relative to the SP. As you can see, B°TL is visibly longer than H°TL. Again, this is due to the bend in the toe wall. The objective of natural hoof care is to bring B° and B°TL back in alignment with H° and H°TL, respectively. Unfortunately, this can't be achieved through the natural trim alone. As you've probably surmised by now, it will require changes in one of the other 4 Pillars, namely diet, and time to heal as more natural growth emerges.

Figure P3-8 depicts pathological changes in H° and H°TL due to unnatural hoof care

Figure P3-6

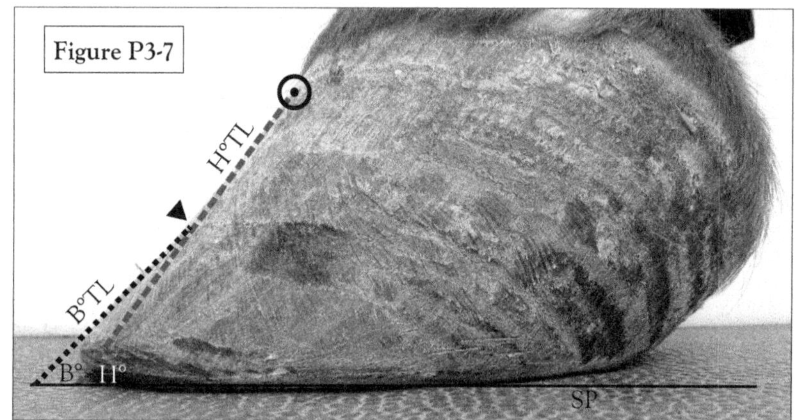

Figure P3-7

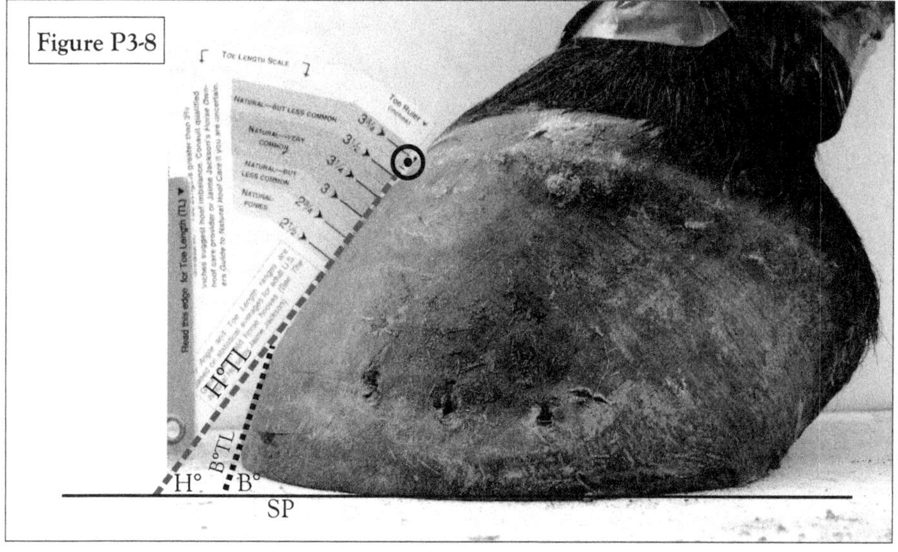

Figure P3-8

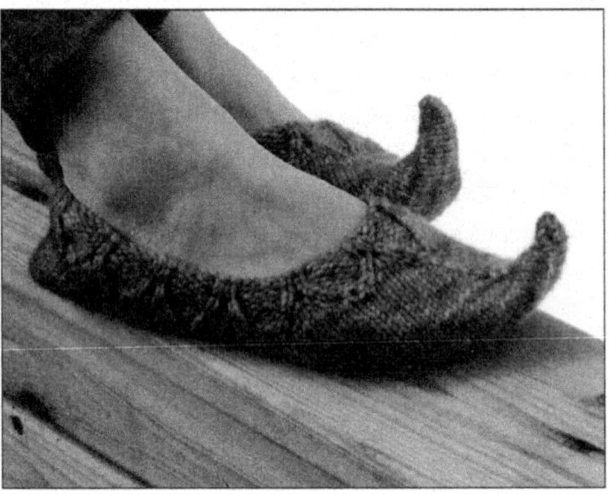

practices, specifically, rasping away the toe wall. As you can see, B°TL has corrupted behind H°TL and, as a result, H°TL now measures less than H°TL in length, just the opposite of the laminitic hoof. We call this a "bull-nosed" hoof, so named by farriers due to its purported likeness to the snout of a bull! It goes by other names too, including, dubbed toe, backed-up toe, and squared-toe. Whatever you call it, it isn't natural! In contrast, the lower angled laminitic toe is called the "slipper toe" due to its resemblance, particularly so in extreme deformed hooves, to the curled toe of a "Persian slipper!"

Putting it all together

Each *Critical Measurement* (H°, H°TL, B° and B°TL) is measured relative to the *Navigational Landmarks.* So far, we've skirted the specific landmarks, and limited the discussion pretty much to these four measurements. My purpose was to give you an overview of what's coming, which, for the most part will entail you confirming how to find H° and H°TL and measuring accurately. For sure, B° and B° TL will show up too for the reasons I explained – and let me add that it is becoming increasingly difficult for our clinicians to find cadavers that aren't suffering the effects of deep pathology! Hence, from necessity, the ISNHCP provides you with training to find and measure B° and B°TL with hooves suffering from relatively *minor* capsule deformity. This will necessitate using the HMR in a specialized way due to the fact that measurements for both B° and B°TL typically will fall outside Angle Reader and Toe Ruler scales of the HMR. Study assignments for using the HMR on such hooves are provided at the end of this section.

Table P3-1 lists all the *Navigational Landmarks* that you will need to learn to find and mark on the hoof. Most of these can be found on the *Hoof Plexus* illustration in **Figure P3-3.** These must be confirmed by memory and practice in order to proceed beyond the cadaver trim clinic. That's how important they are! Without these, there is no way to find or measure the four *Critical Measurements.*

Table P3-1 – NHC Navigational Landmarks		
Landmark		Purpose
MAVP	*Medial Axis of Volar Profile*	Determine: H°, H°TL, B° and B°TL
MATW	*Medial Axis of Toe Wall*	
Crest of capsule	Highest point on the MATW	
Bull's-eye (1st cm line)	1st point below *Crest of Capsule*	
2nd cm line	2nd point below *Crest of Capsule*	
MPVP	*Median Plane of the Volar Profile*	Determine: *hoof balance* and *heel balance*
MPTW	*Median Plane of the Toe Wall*	
MLHA	*Mediolateral Heel Axis*	

And without those, there is no way to cross-link to the wild horse model. It's the failure, by and large, of the hoof care community – from vets, to farriers, to "generic" barefoot trimmers, to backyard do-it-yourselfers – to understand this relationship that has led to so much harm being done to horses and their hooves. Your job is to change this dreadful course in history and make a difference by linking up with nature according to the wild horse model. *You can do it!*

acronym – a word formed from the first letters of each one of the words in a phrase

The *acronyms* (e.g., MAVP) in the table are typically troublesome for many beginning students to keep straight in their minds. Don't feel discouraged, however, if your mind is beginning to spin around already in your head! You're not alone! But it all passes with a little discipline, and, later, with help from your clinicians in the cadaver trim clinic, where you will use them all. I find it helpful to start saying them aloud, letter by letter, eventually quickly so: M–A–T–W. Your objective is to be *conversant* in our unique NHC language. The acronym enables us to speak in an abbreviated manner. Imagine how long it would take to finish a sentence if we used each word in the acronym! It would take all day to talk about one hoof! And don't worry about sounding "funny" or "peculiar" to others who don't know our language. When we start mixing up "H°TL" (instead of saying, "Healing Angle Toe Length") and other *Critical Measurements* with the Navigational Landmark acronyms, they're probably going to think you're nuts! Outside of us, no one, and I mean no one, will have any idea what you're talking about. That's okay, send them into the training program if they're really interested.

conversant – able to talk in a foreign language; having knowledge or experience

The first five *landmarks* in **Table P3-1** enable us to determine the *Critical Measurements* H°, H°TL, B° and B°TL. The HMR is used to measure H° and H°TL. B° is measurable on the HMR if it falls within the natural angle ranges. When H° falls outside those ranges, the HMR is used differently, discussed below in the study assignments; in such cases, B°TL is always measured with a flexible measuring tape, due to the present of one or more DTAs. The last three landmarks are used to determine *hoof balance* and *heel balance*. The *Hoof Balancer* is used for these two purposes. The HMR, measuring tape, and *Hoof Balancer* are part of your Tools/ Equipment requirement.

Study Assignments
Part 4 – The Importance of Measuring

Assignment #1: Live horse practicum – Over the next seven pages I've adapted the official NHC guidelines you will be using to find and measure H° and H°TL in your cadaver trim clinic. These guidelines are also included in pdf on the DVD you received with other learning materials. The last page of the guidelines includes a data form for the Critical Measurements. Please review my comments regarding filling out this form in the section on the **Cadaver Trim Clinic** on page 117, later in this training manual.

To prepare you in advance for the clinic, go ahead and study these guidelines now. If you own a horse to practice on, apply them to both front hooves, but not the hinds for which there can be safety issues when measuring. The final page includes the *Cadaver and Live Horse Data Form*. Use this form for your horse's measurement data. *Please Note:* 1) Follow the measuring protocols at the bottom of the data form. 2) The instructions are *not* trimming instructions – you will only be marking and measuring the hooves. Trimming *safely* to H° and H°TL requires pre-training on cadavers. To avoid causing harm you should defer trimming your horse until, at the earliest, you have successfully completed the **Live Horse Trim Clinic** (page 119) and you and your clinician feel you are ready.

Assignment #2: PowerPoint Lecture: "Hoof Meter Reader Instructions" – I created this lecture in 2015. Lot's of detail and should pair nicely with the assignment above to help clarify the HMR's use. Refer to Slides 11 through 35 for finding H° and H°TL when they are readable on the HMR data scales.

Assignment #3: Measuring H° and B°TL on hooves suffering minor capsule deformity – These assignments are *not* an invitation for you to trim horses suffering from deep pathology with extreme hoof deformities. They are to enable you to measure and trim hooves that fall only marginally off the H° and H°TL data scales of the HMR. For example, where H° would measure no less than 40 degrees or no more than 70 degrees. Measurements that are less or greater than these "limits" very likely are the providence of the Advanced Trim Guidelines and you should decline trimming such horses. In some cases, H° cannot be read at all due to capsule deformity below ⊙. When this and readings below and above the limits (40 and 70 degrees, respectively) are the case, then the HMR is used in a specialized manner in order to conduct safe measurements with equally safe cut-lines. Students who, for whatever reason, decide to apply these specialized instructions to hooves suffering from extreme capsule deformity, run the extreme risk of putting horses in significant harm's way. Once more, students should decline to trim such hooves until such time that they are qualified to do so by completing the Advanced Natural Trim Training Program. Alternatively, motivated students should bring the owners of such horses to the attention of the ISNHCP for consultations, or direct them to the Practitioner Locator List of qualified trimmers identified on the AANHCP website.

- ***The Natural Trim: Principles and Practice* — Chapter 6: "The Healing Angle (H°) and Other Critical Measurements"** — There are discussions of why and how we use the HMR to "approximate" H° in deformed hooves. Examples include deformed hooves, most of which fall into the category of extreme capsule deformity. Nevertheless, the instructions apply to more moderate degrees of deformity. Study pages 114 through 123. Use this information in conjunction with the PowerPoint lecture below that you may find clearer for applying the HMR.
- **PowerPoint Lecture: "Hoof Meter Reader Instructions"** — Refer specifically to Slides 36 through 62 for using the HMR on deformed hooves.
- **The Healing Angle: Nature's Gateway to the Healing Field.** — Study Chapters 6 and 7, which build on previous chapters in this book I assigned earlier.

The above three assignments offer related information for measuring H° on less than naturally shaped hooves. Taken together, they should broaden your perspective on dealing with such hooves.

Step 1 — Hoof Meter Reader Instructions

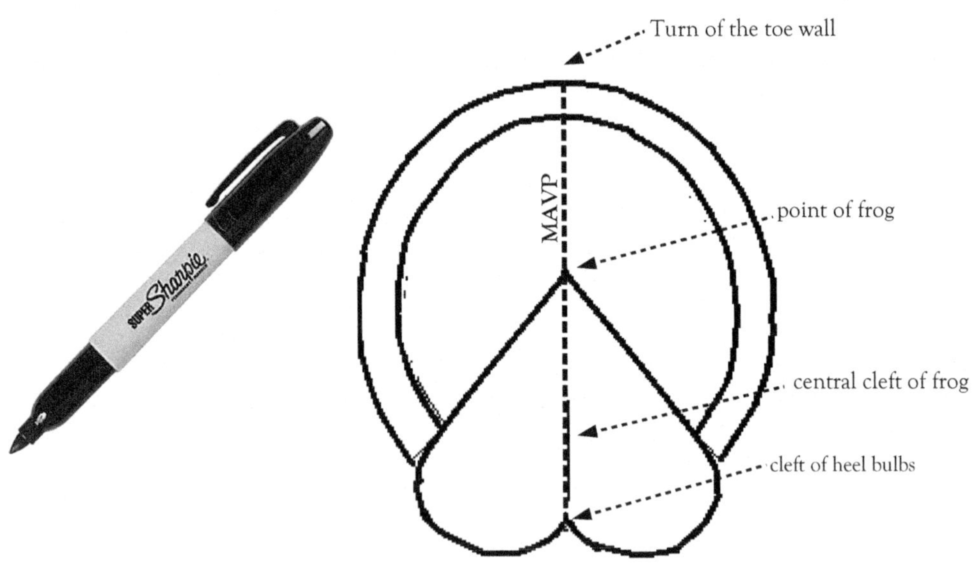

Step 1: Mark the MAVP

Draw a line with a Sharpie pen (black ink) down the middle of the bottom of the hoof. The line should pass through the cleft of the heel bulbs, the central cleft of the frog, and the point of frog. Extend the line all the way to the toe wall and a little ways up the face of the outer wall (Step 2).

§

- This line is called the *Medial Axis of the Volar Profile* (MAVP). "Medial Axis" means "a line down the middle."
- "Volar Profile" means "a representation of the bottom of the hoof."

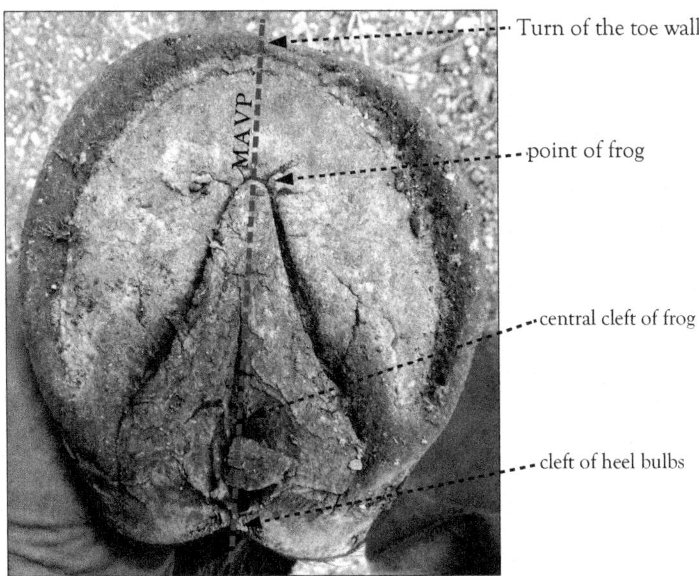

Living example.

Step 2 — Hoof Meter Reader Instructions

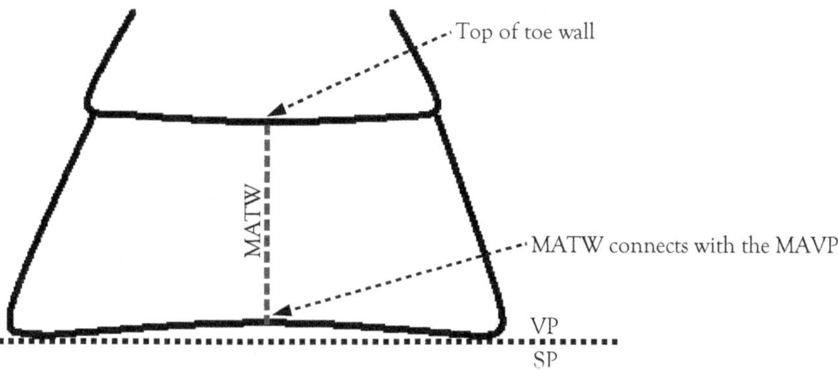

Step 2: Mark the MATW

Extend the line drawn in Step 1 all the way up to the top of the hoof wall where it meets the coronary band. Light pressure with the fingertip will help you locate this point at the top of the wall.

§

- This vertical line is called the *Medial Axis of the Toe Wall* (MATW). This means "a vertical line down the middle of the toe wall."
- The MAVP intersects the MATW at the bottom of the toe wall.

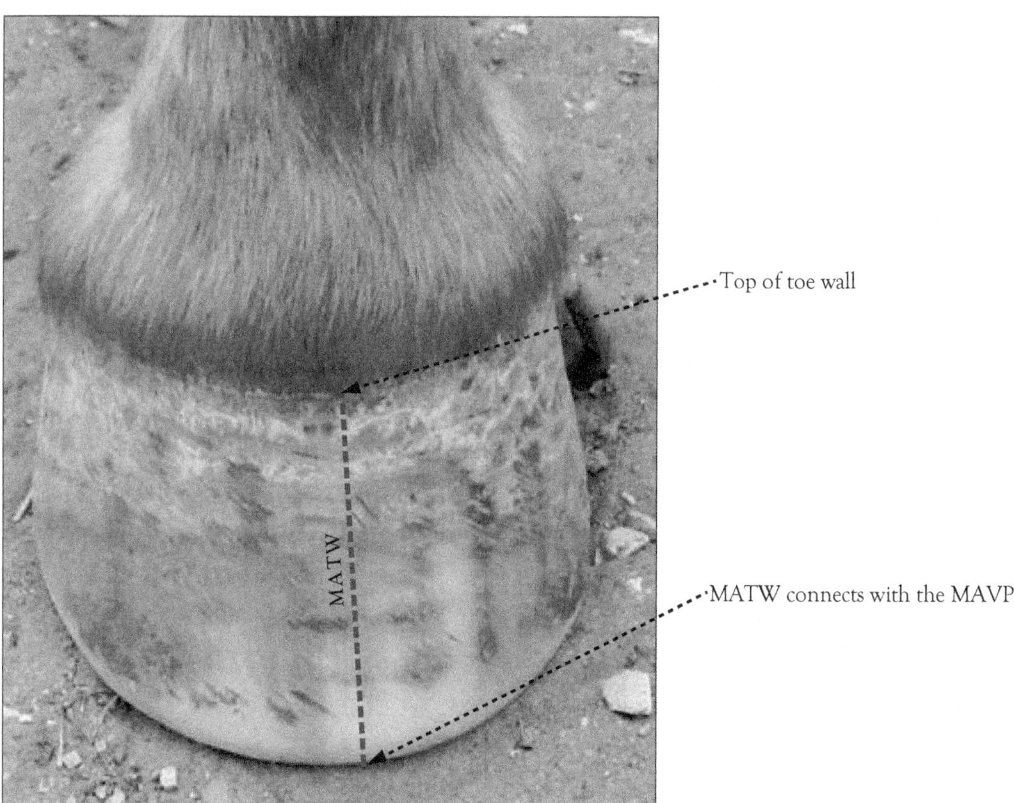

Living example.

Step 3 – Hoof Meter Reader Instructions

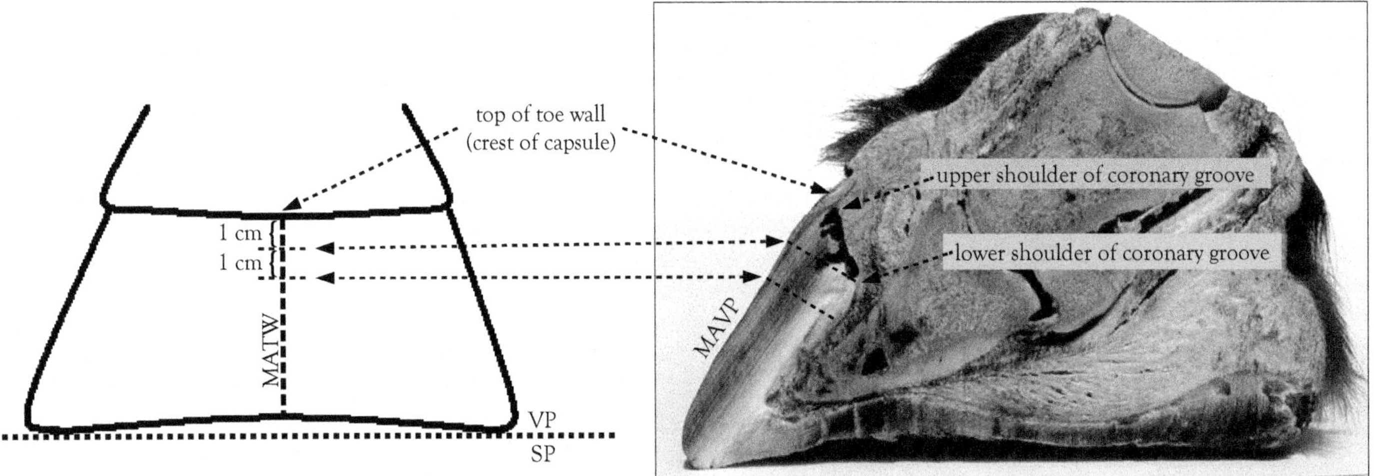

Step 3: Mark lower shoulder of "coronary groove"

Measure down 1 cm from the top of the toe wall (also called "crest of capsule" and draw a short horizontal line. This line corresponds to the lower shoulder of the "coronary groove." Repeat once more, drawing a second horizontal line 1 cm below the first.

§

- The coronary groove houses the "coronary corium" which produces the hoof wall.
- "Coronary" means "crown" or "circlet", meaning encircling the top of the hoof wall. "Corium" means dermis or "live skin" (has nerves and blood vessels).
- "Epidermis" means "outer skin" (no nerves or blood vessels).
- The "hoof" is the epidermis of the horse's foot.

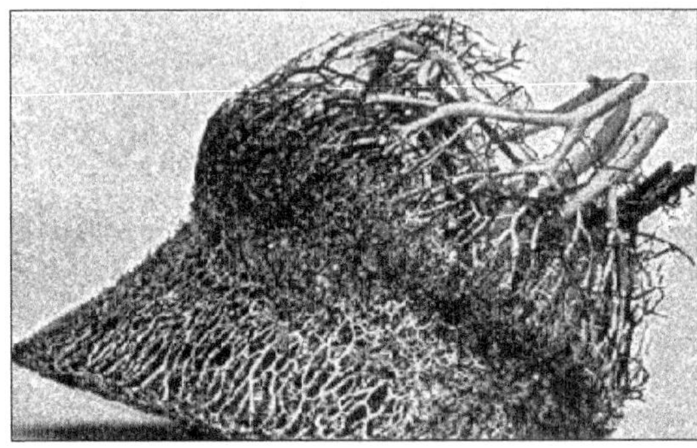

Blood vessels of the horse's foot.

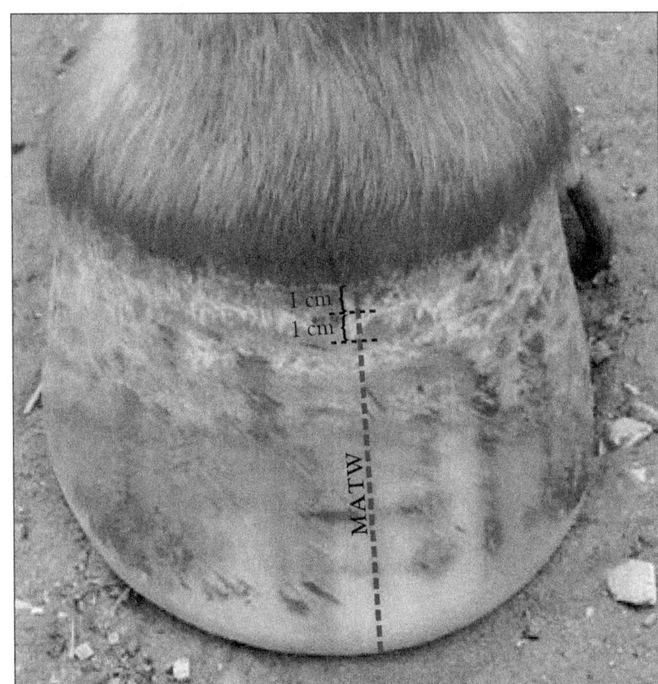

Living example.

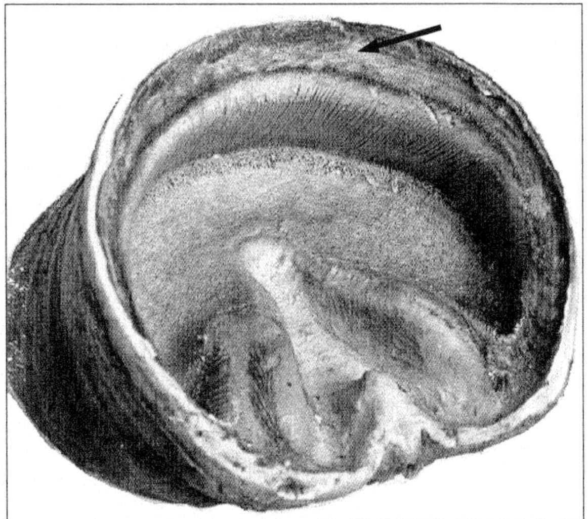

Arrow points to coronary groove.

Step 4 – Hoof Meter Reader Instructions

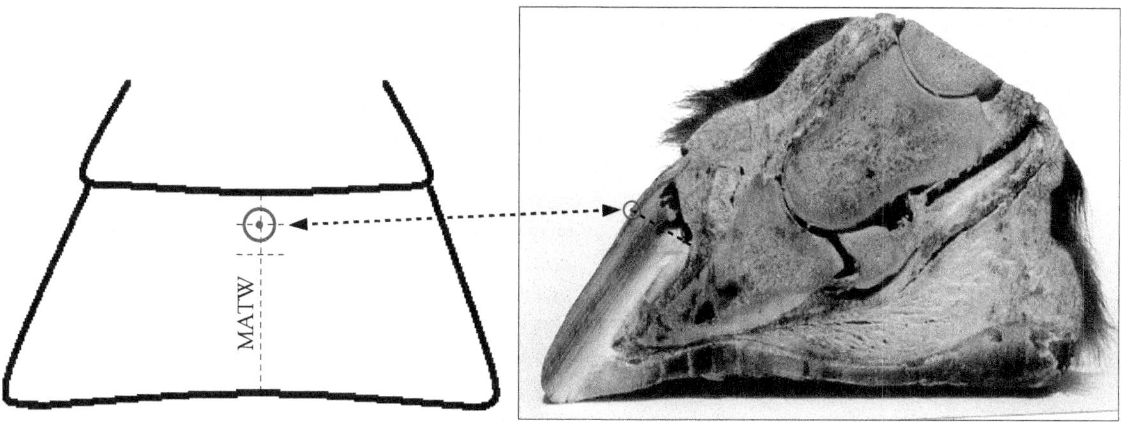

Step 4: Mark the Bull's-eye (⊙)

The upper horizontal line marks the location of the "bull's-eye" on the MATW. This single point on the face of the toe wall enables us to find H° and H°TL. Drawing a circle around this point is helpful in sighting the bull's-eye.

§

- H° is the "Healing Angle"; H°TL is the Healing Toe Length.
- The symbol ⊙ is used to represent the "bull's-eye".
- It is significant that although H° and H°TL are measured in relation to ⊙ on the MATW, neither are measured relative to the MATW! This is explained in Step 5.

Living example.

Step 5 – Hoof Meter Reader Instructions

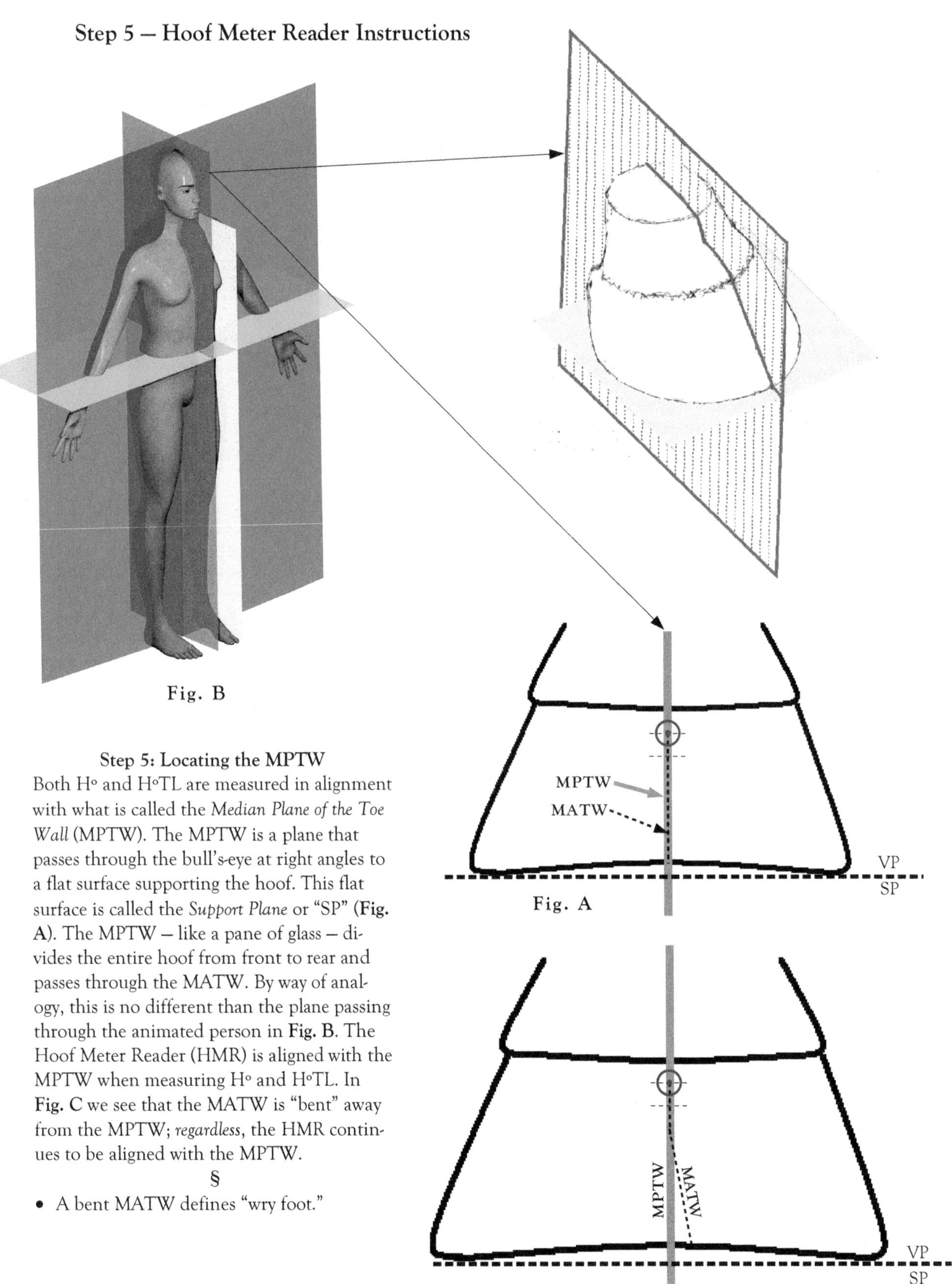

Fig. B

Fig. A

Fig. C

Step 5: Locating the MPTW

Both H° and H°TL are measured in alignment with what is called the *Median Plane of the Toe Wall* (MPTW). The MPTW is a plane that passes through the bull's-eye at right angles to a flat surface supporting the hoof. This flat surface is called the *Support Plane* or "SP" (**Fig. A**). The MPTW – like a pane of glass – divides the entire hoof from front to rear and passes through the MATW. By way of analogy, this is no different than the plane passing through the animated person in **Fig. B**. The Hoof Meter Reader (HMR) is aligned with the MPTW when measuring H° and H°TL. In **Fig. C** we see that the MATW is "bent" away from the MPTW; *regardless*, the HMR continues to be aligned with the MPTW.

§

- A bent MATW defines "wry foot."

Step 6 – Hoof Meter Reader Instructions

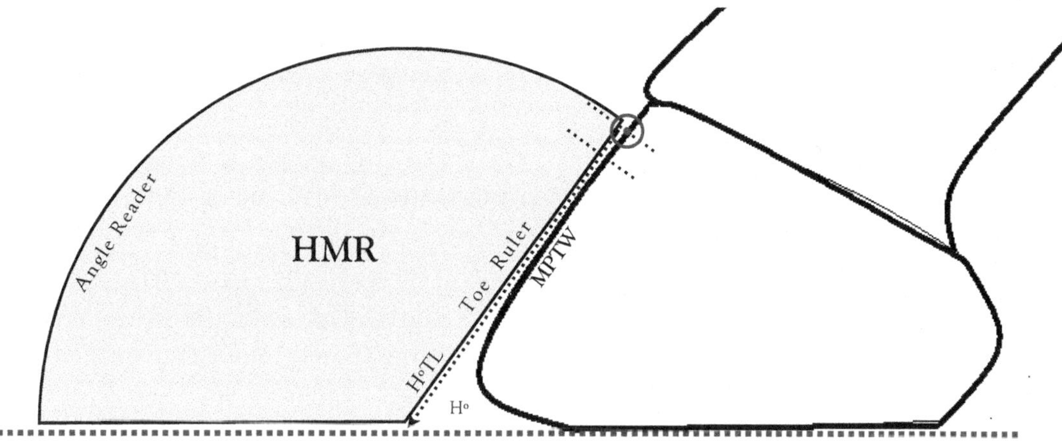

Step 6: Measure H° and H°TL

a) Align the angle arm of the Hoof Meter Reader (HMR) with the MPTW.
b) Rotate the angle dial until it is parallel with the 1 cm segment of toe wall below the bull's eye. Read H° on the angle reader.
c) Next, rotate the Toe Ruler dial of the HMR until it is parallel with the 1 cm segment of toe wall below ⊙. Read H°TL from the bull's-eye to the ground.
d) Enter both measurements into the "Live Horse Data Form".

§

- The HMR below is the "original" version. It's been upgraded to include left and right sides, and now includes both "U.S customary units (e.g., inch}" and "International System of Units (e.g. centimeter)."

ISNHCP Cadaver and Live Horse Data Form

Fill in all information that applies to your training clinic or Field Mentorship

Date: _______ Student's name: ____

Clinician or Field Instructor's name: ______________________________________/_____

Clinician or Field Instructor initial here ▲

Mentorship # _________ Live Horse Clinic # ______ Location __________________________

Cadaver # ___ Horse's name/age/sex/breed ___________________/ ___/ ___/__________

Critical Measurements

	Pre-trim data (Shod/Barefoot)		Post-trim data (fill in last)	
Hoof Balancer Yes/No	LF	RF	LF	RF
H°				
H°TL (⊙ @ 1 cm)				
B°				
B°TL (⊙ @ 1 cm)				
	1st Trim Run (data)		**2nd Trim Run (data)**	
Hoof Balancer Yes/No	LF	RF	LF	RF
H°				
H°TL (⊙ @ 1 cm)				
B°				
B°TL (⊙ @ 1 cm)				
	3rd Trim Run (data)		**4th Trim Run (data)**	
Hoof Balancer Yes/No	LF	RF	LF	RF
H°				
H°TL (⊙ @ 1 cm)				
B°				
B°TL (⊙ @ 1 cm)				

Protocol (Critical Measurements):

1. NHC Navigational Landmarks used to gather all Critical Measurements.
2. Hoof Balancer used to determine Mediolateral Heel Axis (MLHA).
3. Hoof Balancer used to assess location or existence of Support Triad.
4. Hind hooves:
   - No Critical Measurements gathered due to inherent risks of being kicked to head.
   - Authorized use of Hoof Balancer:
     - ◊ MAVP drawn to establish MPVP to mark the MLHA for Heel Balance.
     - ◊ Assess location or existence of Support Triad
   - No kneeling at any time to assess or trim.
   - 3rd and 5th Sequencing Positions only until evaluation by Field Instructors during mentorships authorize taking the 4th Position [**PowerPoint Lecture: Sequencing**].

Quiz (True or False)
Part 3 — Importance of Measuring

These are really important questions. Make sure that you not only get the correct answer, but understand the answer too. If you're having serious issues understanding, form your "student study group" discussed in the manual's introduction.

1. Finding the MPVP is the first step in finding one's way to H°.
2. The MATW terminates at the crest of the capsule.
3. The bull's-eye is located 1 cm below the crest of the capsule.
4. H° is measured parallel to the MATW segment between the upper ($\odot$) and lower horizontal lines.
5. The true hoof wall begins at the lower shoulder of the coronary groove.
6. H°TL is measured from $\odot$ to the VP.
7. H°TL is always measured in alignment with MPTW.
8. A hoof is said to be *wry* when the MATW does not align with the MPVP .
9. B° occurs when the MATW is bent by a DTA.
10. A DTA cannot bend the MPTW.
11. A "slipper toe" occurs when the MATW is bent forward by a DTA.
12. B°TL occurs when the MATW is bent by a DTA.
13. The MPTW and MATW always align.
14. H°TL and MPTW always align.
15. Bull-nose conformation occurs when B° > (is greater than) H°.
16. Slipper toe conformation occurs when H° > B°.
17. B°TL is measured from $\odot$ to the SP.
18. H°TL measures shorter with a tape measure than with the HMR if the MATW terminates in a mustang roll.
19. H° is determined by the length of H°TL relative to the length of the heels.
20. The HMR is calibrated to my wild horse hoof data.

Step 1 – ISNHCP Training Program

Independent Study

Part 4 – Characteristics of the Naturally Shaped Hoof

Mimicking the natural wear patterns of the wild horse hoof defines the natural trim. The *Critical Measurements* tell us how much *epidermal armor we can remove to mimic those wear patterns without causing harm. The Navigational Landmarks* provide us with a road map to where we can measure and make our cuts. The *Hoof Plexus* provides us with a unique geometric image of the hoof that shows us interrelationships of all the parts we will navigate, measure, and trim. It is crucial to understand that this process of mimicking the wear patterns ultimately affects the entire structural character of the hoof, including the cycles of growth patterns that will follow in the wake of the trim. Thus, hooves trimmed according to our guidelines for the natural trim, and in conjunction with the *4 Pillars of NHC*, will yield naturally shaped hooves [**Figure P4-1**]. In contrast, hooves trimmed according to other methods not based on these guidelines will yield unnaturally shaped hooves, some blatantly grotesque and, by any humane standard, criminally negligent. Images of these types of hooves can be seen in *Laminitis: An Epidemic.*

I've included below discussions of those characteristics of the naturally shaped hoof that feature prominently in how we conduct the natural trim.

Mustang Roll

The "mustang roll" is a unique wear characteristic of the wild horse hoof wall. Greatly simplified, it represents the somewhat rounded turn of the entire hoof wall from toe to heel [**Figure P4-2**]. This is a critical wear pattern to mimic during the course of the basic natural trim guidelines. Properly done, there are several significant outcomes:

- Contributes to natural wall growth.
- Contributes to the hoof wall's structural stability.
- Contributes to *hoof balance.*
- Facilitates locomotive stability (e.g., natural gaits).

Shaping the mustang roll is complex and is taken up later in the Part 10 (Steps 5 and 7, pages 112 and 114 respectively) trimming instructions of this training manual.

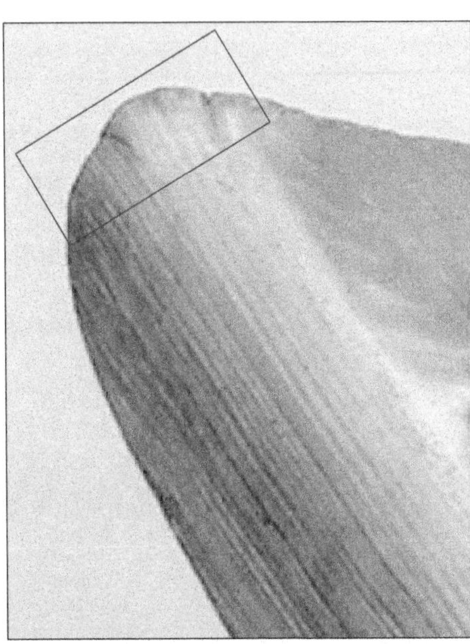

Figure P4-2. Blue rectangle brackets the mustang roll at the ground-bearing end of the hoof wall in cross-section.

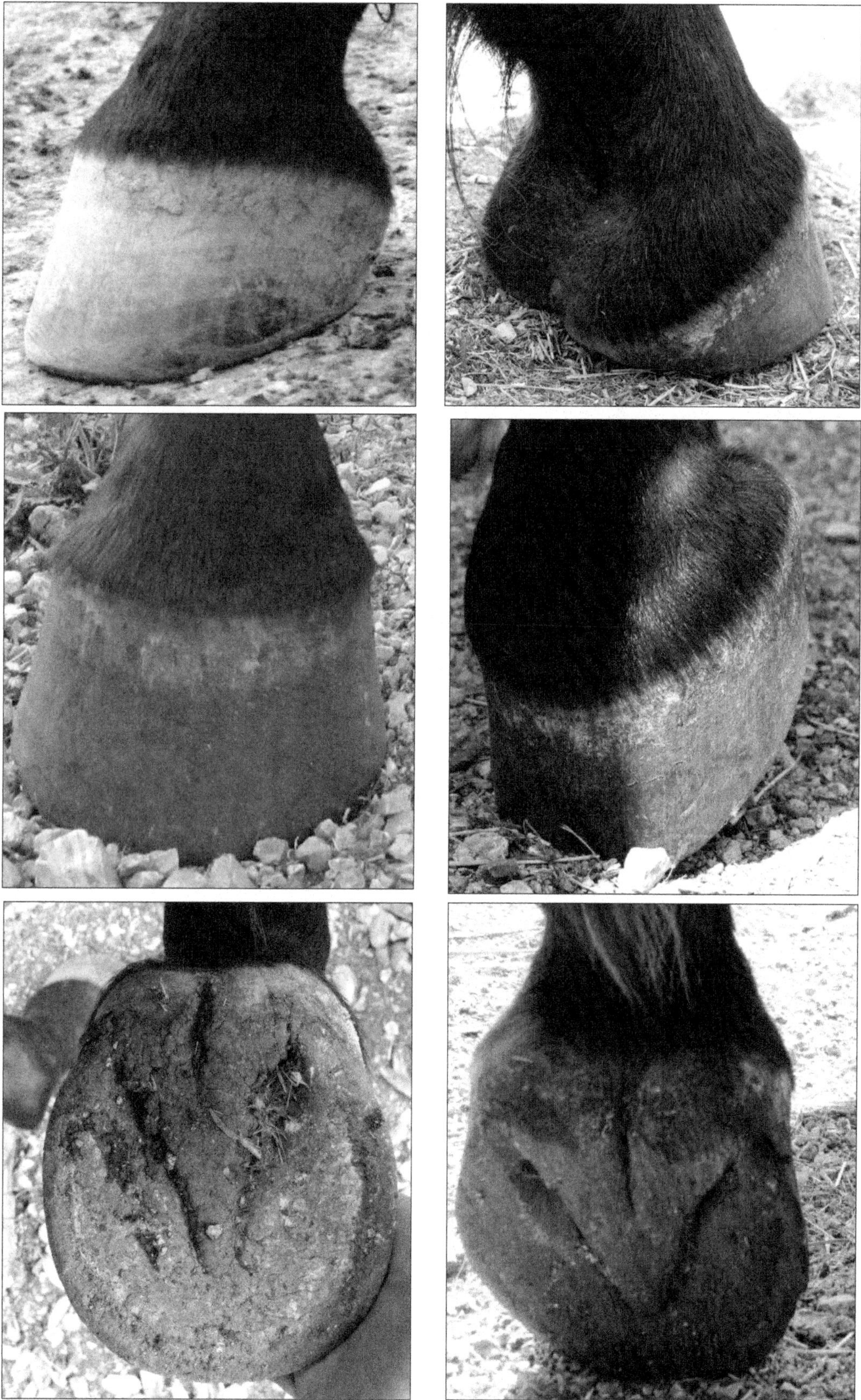

Figure P4-1. Examples of sound, healthy exemplary hooves trimmed according to ISNHCP guidelines. The horses live outdoors 24/7 at the AANHCP Field Headquarters on the central coast of California.

Front versus hind hooves

Wild horse hooves have very unique shapes and sizes when we evaluate them from left to right, and from front to hind. While my research revealed that there is considerable variation across wild horse populations in terms of hoof proportion – size, length, and angle of growth – certain characteristics were shared by all horses. The mustang roll, just described, is one example. Of particular interest to me was what I would find relative to front and hind hooves. I suspected that nature would enable certain patterns in the hoof's morphology, and that turned out to be the case. So, as part of your learning, let's look at some of these characteristics because, to some extent, how we trim the hooves will either favor or compromise their stability.

Size (Volar)

volar – underside of the foot

What I found was that, for any given horse, left and right hooves varied very little to nothing in *volar* size (ie., from side to side, and front to back) from left to right [**Figure P4-3**]. Statistically, they were identical. However, front hooves were statistically larger than hinds for the same horse. Most of this difference centered around the toe region of the hooves – fronts were rounder.

Toe Length

I measured hoof length (N°TL) at the toe. Statistically, left and right, front and hind, were the same for any given horse.

Toe Angle

I measured hoof angle (N°) at the toe. Statistically, left and right hooves were the same for any given horses. However, on average, N° for hind hooves measure about 3 degrees higher than front hooves for any given horse.

Shape: Symmetry and Asymmetry

Another significant and contrasting characteristic of front versus hind feet concerns hoof wall "symmetry" and "asymmetry." This refers to the peripheral shape of the hoof wall when viewed from *below*, *front* and *above*.

When viewed from ***below***, both front and hinds divide symmetrically down the middle (MAVP), meaning each side is a "mirror image" of the other in terms of size and shape [**Figure P4-3**].

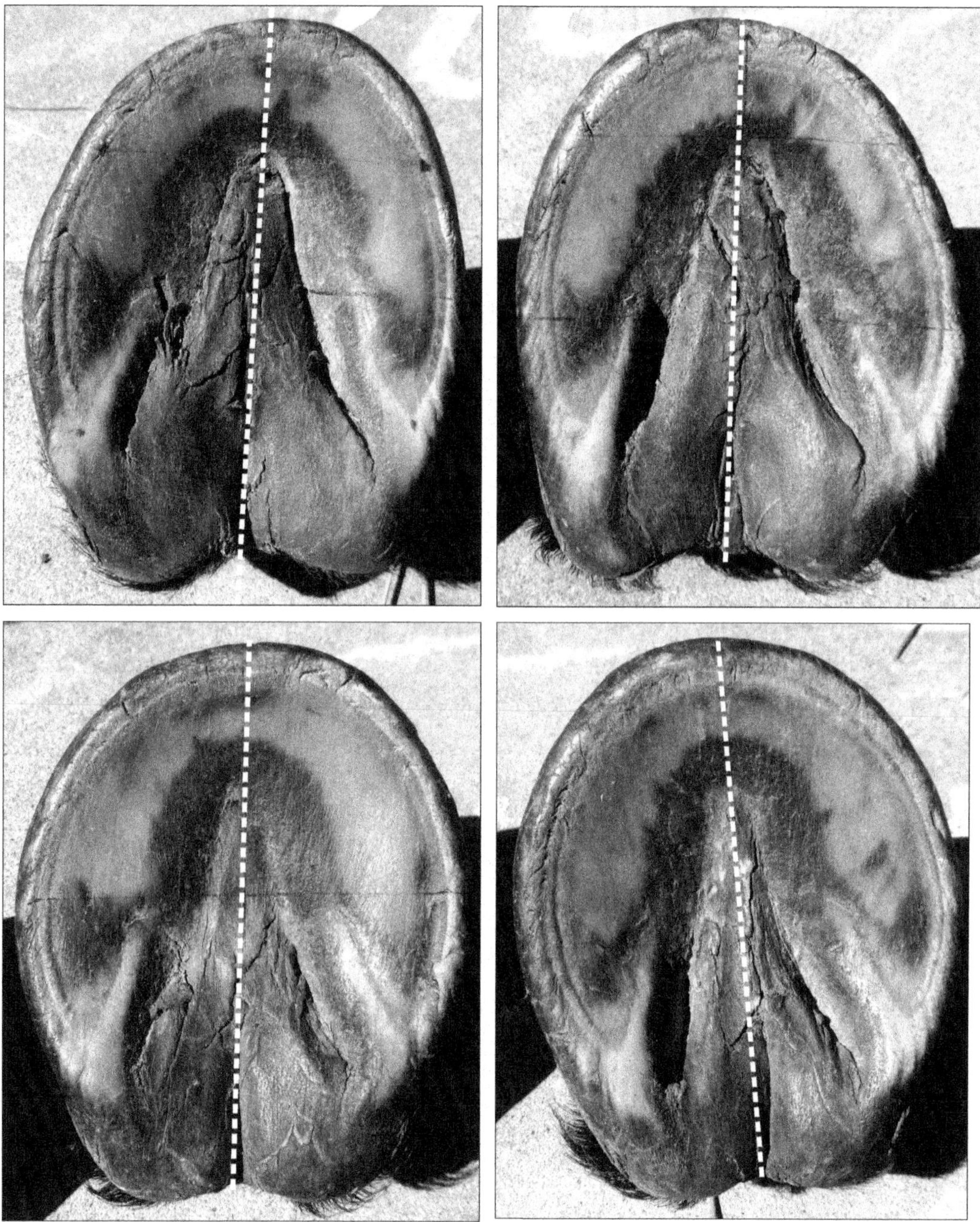

Figure P4-3. (*Top*) Left and right hind wild hooves. (*Bottom*) Left and right front wild hooves. *White dashed lines* (MAVP) bisect – divide in half – all the hooves.

Viewed from the ***front***, differences between front and hinds emerge: front hooves divide symmetrically across the MATW – meaning the medial and lateral sides [**Figure P4-4**] are mirror images of each other; hinds divide asymmetrically on either side of the MATW, so they are not mirror images of each other [**Figure P4-5, *above***]. When viewed from ***above***, we see the same front/hind, symmetry/asymmetry differences when viewed from the front [**Figure P4-5, *below***].

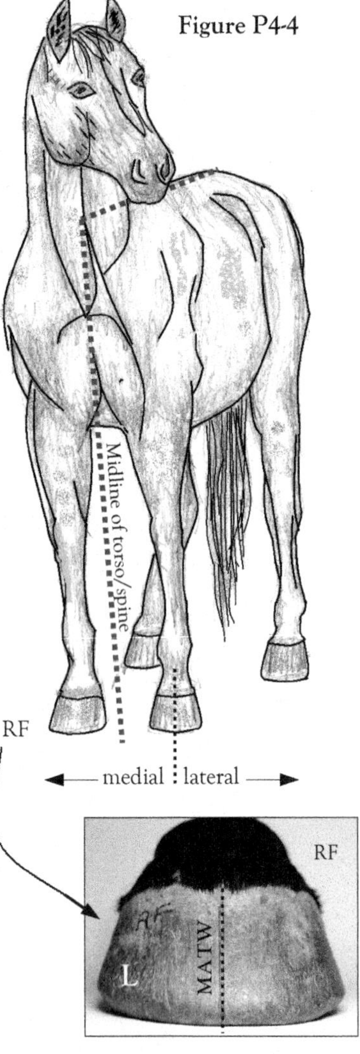

Figure P4-4

Angle of Growth

A unique characteristic of the hoof wall my studies revealed – and reported for the first time in the hoof care literature – is its changing angle of growth from the toe (steepest angle) to the heels (lowest angle) [**Figure P4-5**]. This growth pattern has implications for how we trim hooves. One often hears from trimmers, "Why do I always have to nip off more heel than toe?" Or from horse owners, "My horse sure grows a lot of heel." The answer lies in how the hoof wall grows down and how it is trimmed. To sustain the same angle of growth at the toe (e.g., H°) more heel will have to be trimmed away than at the toe. As *delineated* in **Figure P4-6**, this is because the heel wall grows at a lower angle, thus, a greater length of heel wall must be removed for every equivalent length of toe wall removed.

delineate – to indicate or represent by drawn lines

So, why this variance in angle of growth? I've speculated that one of two things is happening if the hoof's toe angle (N° or H°) is to remain the same year around, evidenced by my data collected in both summer and winter months. Either heel growth occurs slower than toe wall growth, or, more wear occurs naturally over the heels than at the toe. But in observing the typical overgrown hooves of domestic horses, we find proportionally more heel growth than at the toe. This suggests that heel growth naturally occurs at a greater rate than at the toe, but is selected by nature to endure greater wear. The stability of N° and the massive heel-buttresses of the wild hoof support this conclusion.

I believe there are clinical implications for shoeing horses as a result of this variance in angle of growth. Because when growth goes unchecked, particularly if the heels are left intentionally too long before the shoe is applied, the hoof's natu-

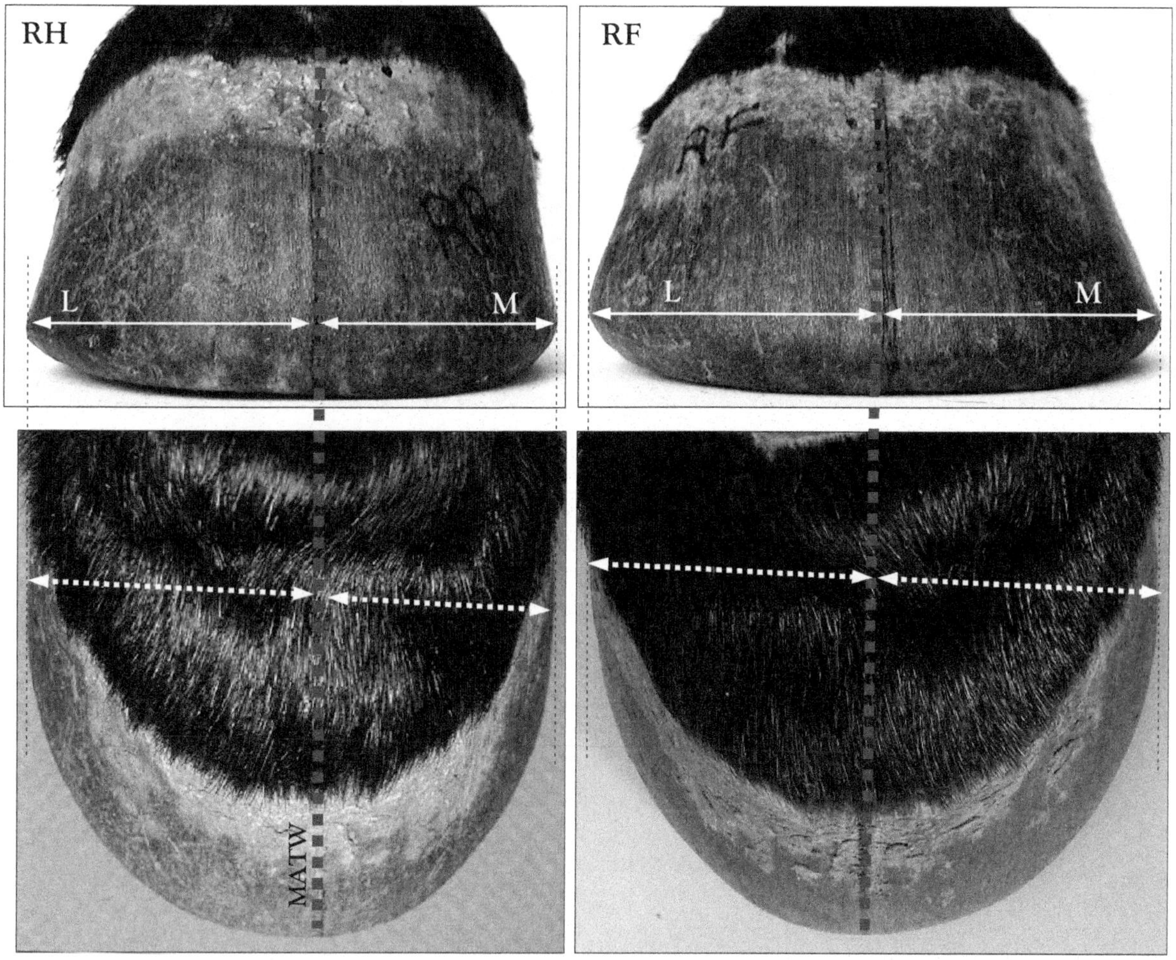

Figure P4-5, above. Right front (RF) and right hind (RH) wild hooves. *M* and *L* marks the medial and lateral walls of each hoof. *Dashed blue lines* mark the medial axis (MATW) established in the volar profile (MAVP). Right front *M* and *L* arrows are the same length reflecting the symmetric divisions in this profile; in contrast, the right hind medial arrow is shorter than the lateral arrow, typical of naturally shaped hind hooves. **Below.** *Dashed blue lines* extend to the same hooves in superior view, revealing the same symmetric/asymmetric conformations.

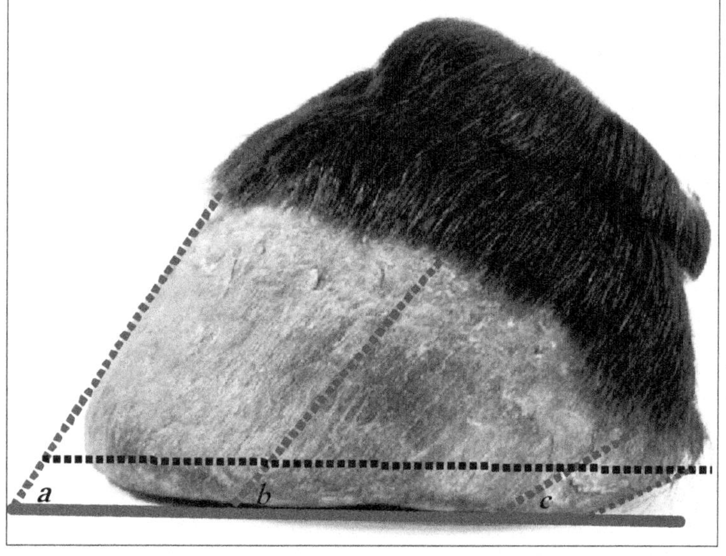

Figure P4-6. *Blue dashed lines* parallel the hoof's angle of growth from toe ("a") to heel ("c"). *Black dashed line* represents a hypothetical cut-line parallel to SP that does not change the hoof's natural toe angle (H°). To sustain H° more heel will have to be trimmed away than at the toe. This can be seen in the wall segments *a*, *b*, and *c*, where they are progressively longer from toe to heel.

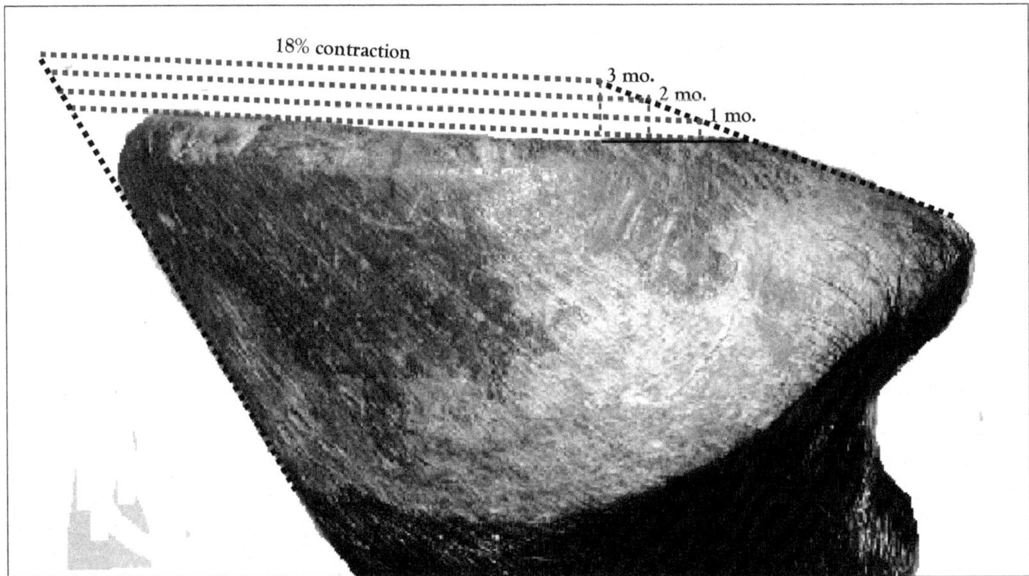

Figure P4-7. *Blue dashed lines* represent the shrinking support base of the hoof over time (hoof growth rate of 1 cm/month) if this hoof were shod. I've done the math and the rate of contraction is approximately 6%/month. Typically, horses are shod every 2 months, some longer, some until they fall off. While this is ominous in its own right, we see also that the contracting support base is also migrating dangerously forward with each passing month. Imagine if you yourself were forced to walk in shoes that kept getting smaller by the day, and at the same moving forward of your center of gravity. Not a pretty picture! By definition, shoeing (and barefoot trim methods that ignore this natural characteristic of the capsule's angle of growth) inherently compromise the horse's ability to move naturally and predispose him to lameness.

ral support base continues to do two things simultaneously: It shrinks by approximately 6% per month (growth rate 1 cm/mo) and migrates forward of its natural position at the rate of approximately ¼ inch (.64 cm) per month [**Figure P4-7**]. Due to neglect and incompetence, some migrations rise to the level of animal abuse and criminality (*facing page*). It is hard to imagine that a typical 1,000 lb. animal losing this much contracted and displaced support mass per month, won't have some bearing on their ability to move naturally, and the high incidence of documented lameness in domesticated horses. According to Walt Taylor, co-founder of the American Farriers Association, and a member of the World Farriers Association and Working Together for Equines programs:

> Of the 122 million equines found around the world, no more than 10 percent are clinically sound. Some 10 percent (12.2 million) are clinically, completely and unusably lame. The remaining 80 percent (97.6 million) of these equines are somewhat lame . . . and could not pass a soundness evaluation or test.
> [American Farriers Journal, Nov./2000, v. 26, #6, p. 5.]

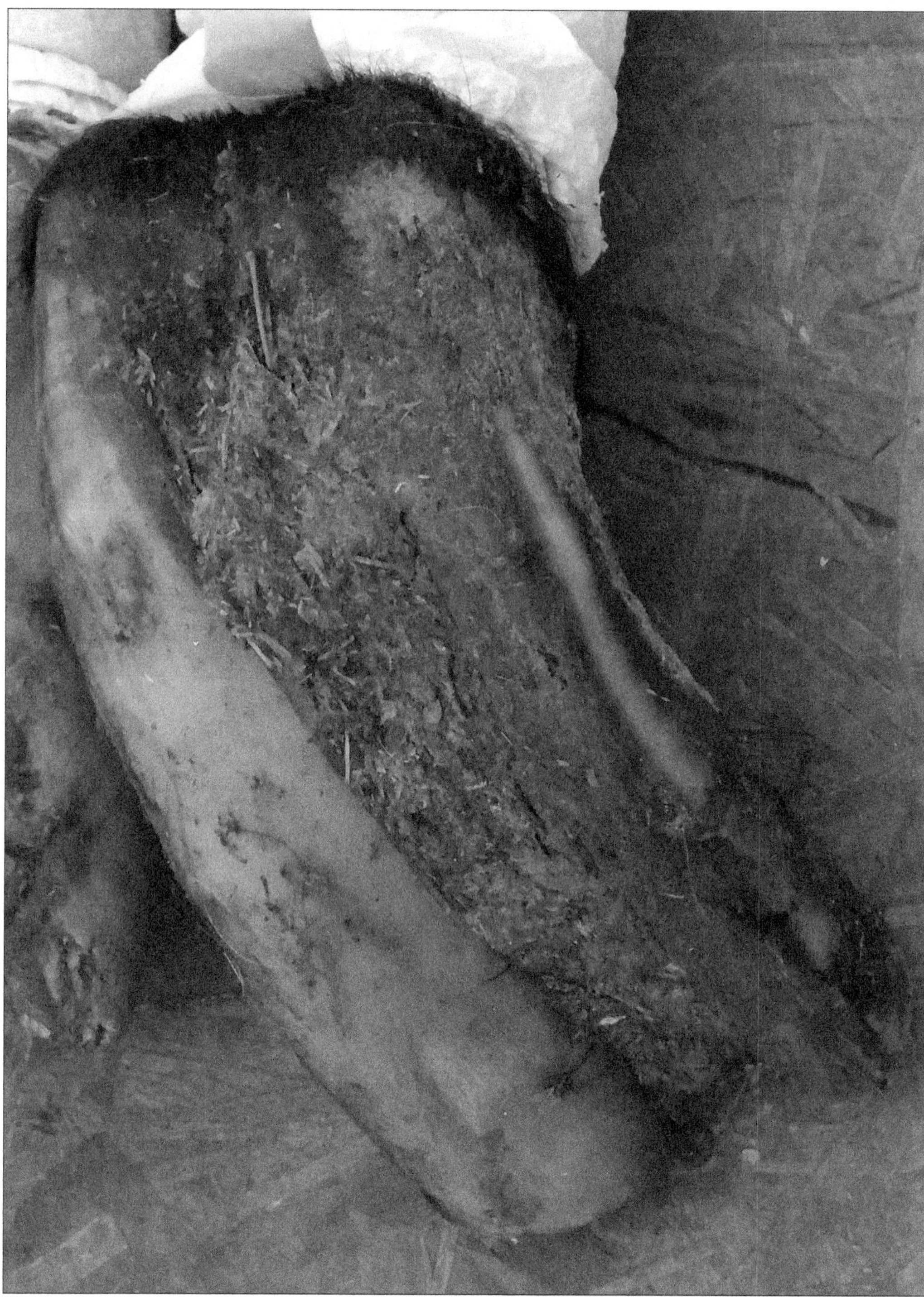

This hoof was allowed to grow into grotesque deformity, ending in a wried "tube" shape. The end of the hoof wall, however, was shortened with a hacksaw, indicating a "method" of sorts was in play. What this means is that the hoof was in a "run away" mode and no one involved knew what to do. Our NHC Advanced Trim Guidelines would have solved the problem readily – the Navigational Landmarks with cut-lines drawn down to the millimeter in just a few minutes.

Step 1 – ISNHCP Training Program

Independent Study

Part 5 - What is Hoof Balance?

One of the most controversial and perplexing problems of hoof care concerns the meaning of *hoof balance*. In other words, what constitutes a naturally balanced hoof? The wild horse model is very clear on what this means, but represents a significant and welcome departure from conventional veterinary, farriery, and generic barefoot concepts, interpretations and what is clearly just plain nonsense. From our model, I was able to *synthesize* a working method for balancing the hooves based on the interrelationships between the following:

synthesize – to combine (things) in order to make something new

- *Active and passive wear patterns of the hoof wall*
- *Orientation of the horn tubules ("grain") of the outer hoof wall*
- *H°TL*
- *Hard sole plane* (HSP)
- *Frog and hard frog plane (HFP)*
- *Heel balance*

Each of these elements contribute to the meaning of hoof balance, and all are derived directly from wild horse hooves.

Active and passive wear patterns of the hoof wall

Active and *passive wear* are significant characteristics of the naturally shaped hoof. They are the natural convolutions of the hoof wall's ground-bearing surface. Unlike the "flat shod" hoof wall of the farrier, the naturally shaped hoof wall at ground level is anything but flat! Meaning, certain segments of the wall are more protruding than others. The more protruding segments are defined as "active wear" or "support pillars"; areas of recession between active wear are defined as "passive wear" [**Figure P5-1**]. *Active wear*, therefore, is associated with *active support*, whereas *passive wear* means *passive support*. There's an analogy with people who go barefoot: areas of active wear (like the ball or heel) typically are callused; areas of passive wear (e.g., the arch of the foot) tend to be less callused. Active wear for both our species are an epidermal response to greater wear forces.

We discussed earlier in Part 3 [**Figure P3-2**], that specific areas of active and passive wear are technically defined by the relationship of the hoof's *volar plane* (VP) to a *support plane* (SP). We learned that active wear along the VP makes physical contact with the SP, passive wear does not. My research showed that in the naturally balanced hoof there are three areas of active wear, or *support pillars* [**Figure P5-2**]:

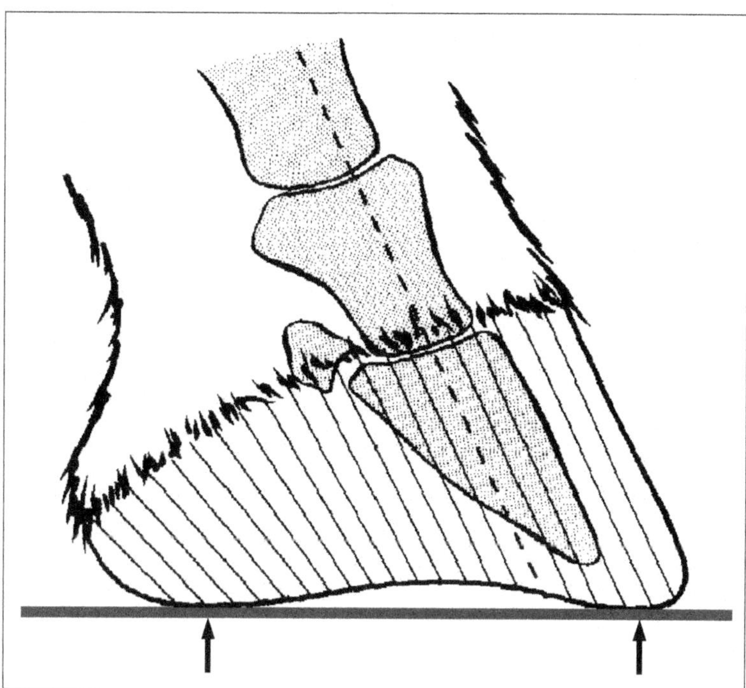

Figure P5-1. *Arrows* point to segments of *active wear* (support). The expanse of hoof wall between the arrows is *passive wear* (support).

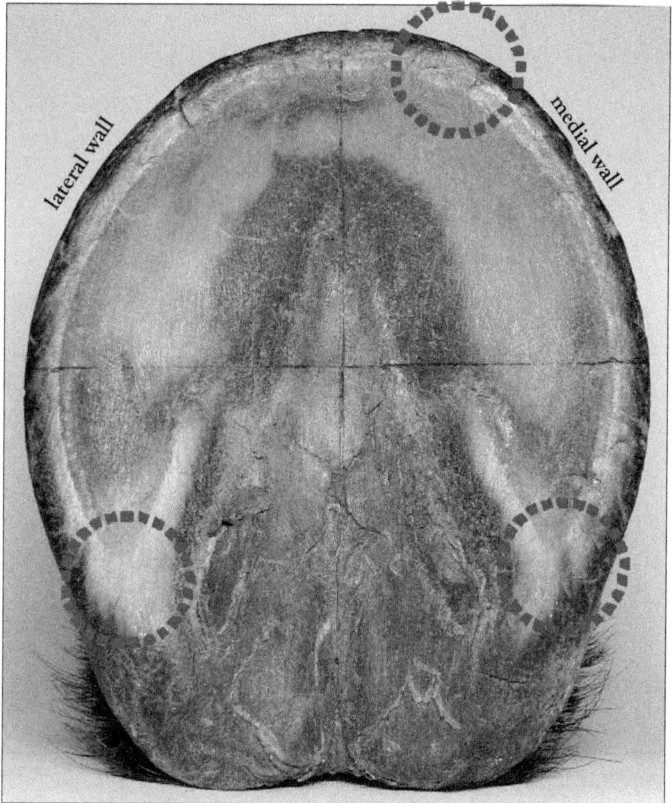

Figure P5-2. *Dashed circles* mark the location of *active wear* (*support pillars*) over both heels and one segment on the medial toe wall, on a right front wild horse hoof cadaver.

both heels and one segment of the toe wall. Moreover, with few exceptions, toe wall pillars occurred on the medial side of the hoof [**Figure P4-5**] – the side closest to the horse's midline [**Figure P4-4**]. Because they typically occur in groups of 3 (medial toe wall and both heels), these support pillars are also called *support triads.*

triad – a group of three

One might ask: why is there active and passive wear, why isn't the hoof just flat like a horseshoe, and why does the toe pillar typically occur along the medial toe wall? My research revealed a diverse variation in the temperaments and conformations of wild horses. I reasoned that the active and passive wear I observed reflected these differences. As support pillars, I concluded that each active wear pillar served like a callus on the human foot or hand. Active wear, in other words, reflected areas of increased locomotive (weight-bearing) force on the hoof wall. According to this rationale, the dermis that creates the hoof wall, responding to weight-bearing and ground generated concussional forces through its nerve bed, produces more epidermis (forming the pillars of the support triad) to offset wear and sustain both the horse's stationary and locomotive balance - less the hoof grow awry and imperil the natural gaits altogether. Conversely, areas of passive wear, logically, are fortified with less epidermal armor because there is less *concentrated* locomotive force in those expanses of the hoof wall. Later, I confirmed this hypothesis by observing the emergence and location of active and passive wear in horses I de-shod and trimmed to our guidelines.

As we shall see, *active wear* technically defines "hoof balance," providing the hoof has otherwise been trimmed to our guidelines (Steps 3 and 4 of the trimming guidelines in this training manual, page 110).

Orientation of tubular horn

The hollow, hair-like fibers called *tubular horn* that comprise the epidermal "armor" of the hoof was discussed earlier in this manual [**Part 2 –Epidermal Structures**]. We recall that they constitute the "grain" visible in the outer hoof wall, and throughout the hoof wall itself [**Figure P5-3**]. When the hoof wall is viewed from the front, the growth orientation of the

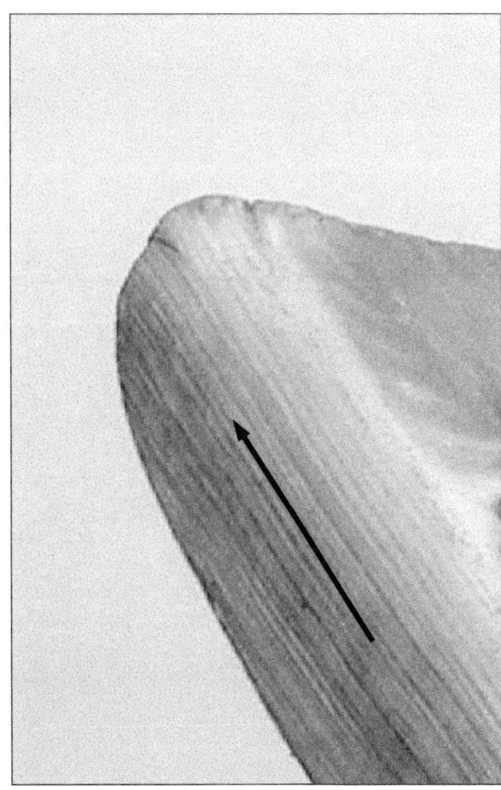

Figure P5-3. Arrow aligns with layers upon layers of cemented tubular fibers, which constitute the hoof wall seen here in cross-section.

Figure P5-4. Nipper dragging is a technique of prying loose sole epidermis away in order to locate the HSP. The sole corium extrudes flat layers of epidermis called *solar plates*. As new plates are produced at the *live sole plane* [**Figure P2–1**], older plates are worn or trimmed away at the *hard sole plane*. In the wild and in some Paddock Paradises, older plates readily shed after approximately 1 cm of growth. To remove older plates, the outside blade is braced lightly against the outer hoof wall; the other blade is "dragged" across the sole to the hoof wall. This criminally neglected hoof (a cadaver) will require 3 to 4 "drag and trim runs" to reach the HSP. When the HSP at the toe is finally confirmed, H°TL can then be measured accurately with the HMR.

grain lies roughly at ninety degrees (90°) to its VP. This vertical orientation of the grain is yet another defining characteristic of the balanced hoof.

H°TL

H°TL, the shortest possible length of the toe wall that can be trimmed without penetrating the HSP, defines the hoof's forward most parameter for establishing hoof balance. Until H°TL is confirmed, it is not possible to balance the hoof in accordance with NHC Guidelines for the natural trim. Determining the precise location of the HSP is one of the great challenges of NHC, and is a central focus of the ISNHCP training program in the **Cadaver Trim Clinic**.

Hard Sole Plane (HSP)

The HSP is determined through the technique of "nipper dragging" [**Figure P5-4**] in conjunction with the HMR's *toe ruler*. Both require acquiring skills that come from training, practice, and experience. The first objective is to establish the HSP where the MATW intersects the toe wall. Once that is accomplished, nipper dragging continues posteriorly (towards the back of the hoof), terminating in each seat-of-corn. The finished HSP forms a single plane from toe to each heel. Your clinician will demonstrate and guide you through the entire process of dragging, measuring, and finishing the entire HSP.

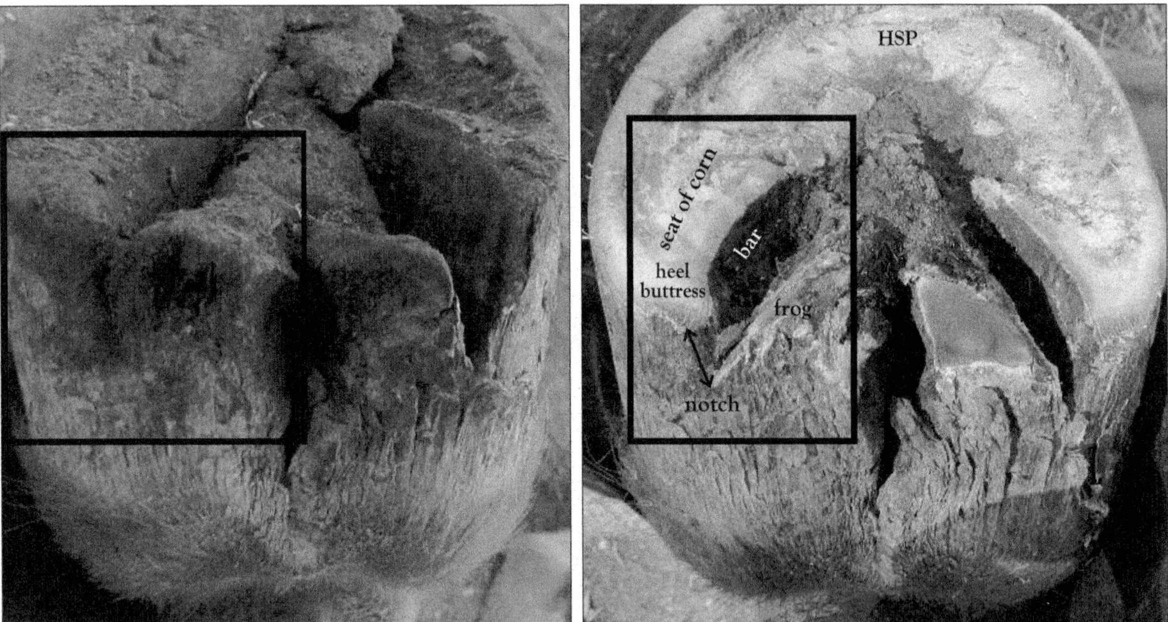

Figure P5-5. *Black boxes* highlight *pre–* and *post–* frog "notching," a useful technique to identify heel length. *Double arrow* (↔) marks *heel length.*

Frog and Hard Frog Plane (HFP)

The frog plays a key role in establishing hoof balance because other nearby structures (bars, seats-of-corn, and heel buttresses) are trimmed relative to its natural proportions. The task here is two-fold: first, trimming the frog down to its own *hard frog plane* (HFP) – similar to the *hard sole plane* (HSP); second, using a specialized technique called "notching," the frog is trimmed down to its epidermal juncture with the bars at the very rear of the heel-buttresses [**Figure P5-5**]. Indirectly, the purpose of this is to determine actual heel length. So accomplished, the trimmer is then ready to shorten and balance the heels.

Heel balance

Marking and balancing the heels, and trimming the remaining hoof wall from toe to heel down to the HSP, concludes the process of balancing the hoof. You will use the *Hoof Balancer* [**Figure P5-6**] to mark the heels and establish a single cut-line – called the *mediolateral heel axis* (MLHA) – across both heels and the frog [**Figure P5-7**]. Everything above this *composite* cut-line is considered a "safe cut" – meaning, by definition, nowhere will the HSP be penetrated.

composite – made up of distinct parts or elements

The last thing done to balance the hoof is to lower the entire hoof wall to H° TL and MLHA following the HSP. This is done with the nippers and will be an

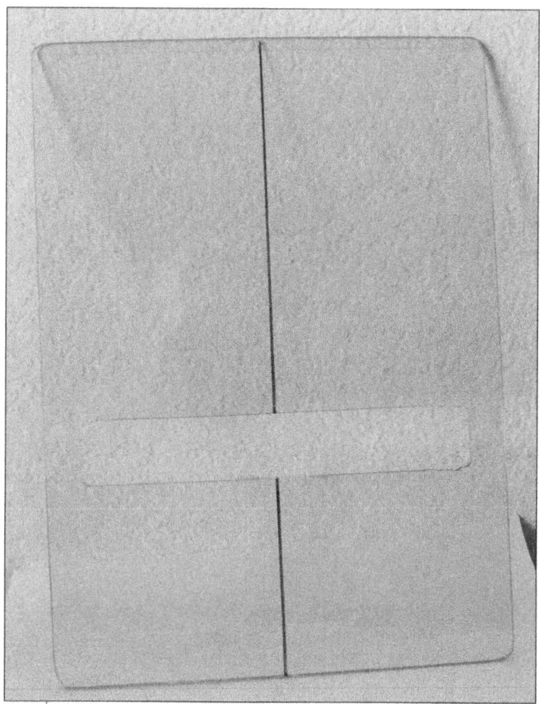

Figure P5-6. *Hoof Balancer*

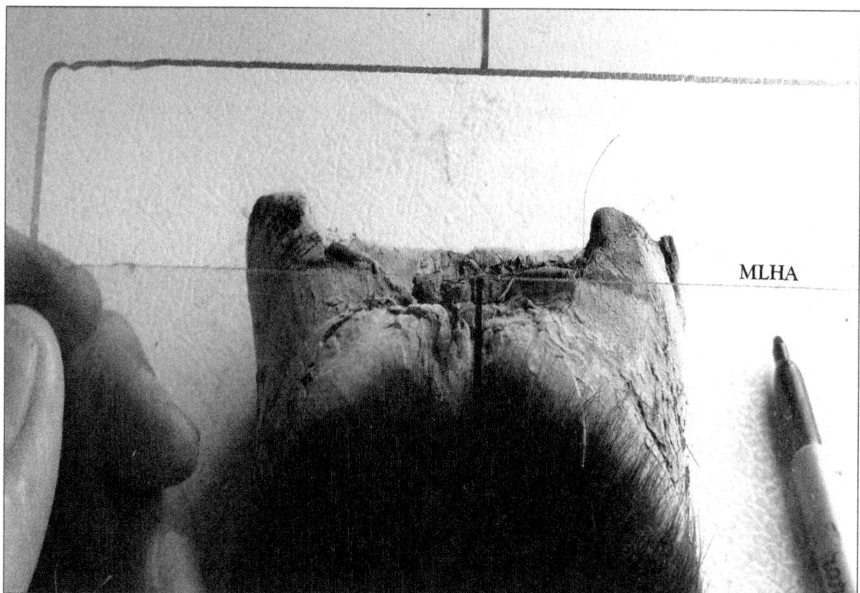

Figure P5-7. The *MLHA* follows along the lower window edge of the simulated *Hoof Balancer*. Sharpie is used to mark the back of each heel. This is a cadaver hoof.

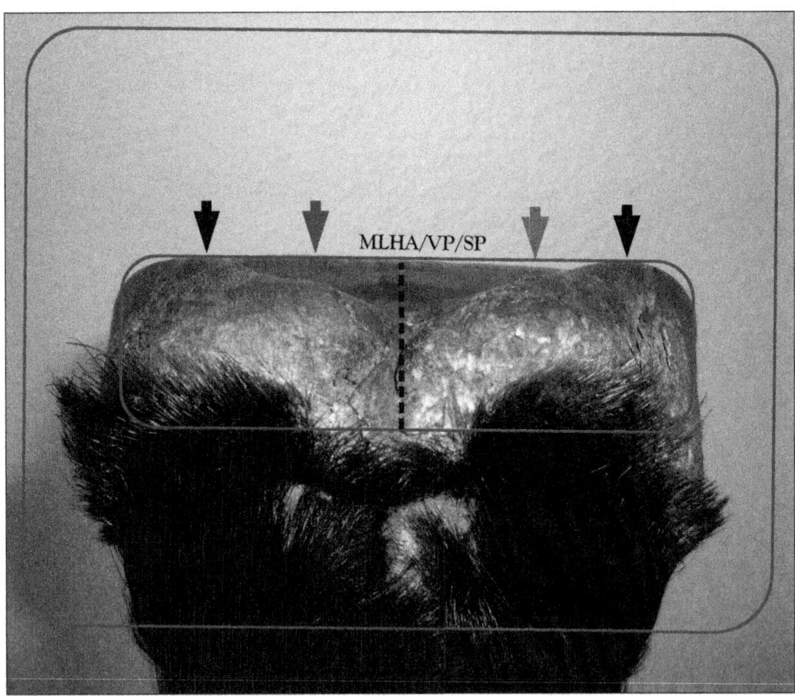

Figure P5-8. *Hoof balance defined.* Simulated *Hoof Balancer* window positioned over wild horse hoof in its posterior view. The upper window edge of the *Hoof Balancer* is aligned with the MLHA, VP, and SP. The *black dashed line* is the MPVP. *Black arrows* point to heel support pillars on the MLHA; *blue arrow* points to medial toe wall pillar; *red arrow* points to area of passive wear along lateral toe wall. Can you deduce if this is a left or right hoof? [Answer: it's a left hoof since the toe wall pillar (*blue arrow*) is located on the medial side of the hoof. Note too that the frog in this view of the hoof is indistinguishable from the heel-buttresses. This is very typical of naturally worn hooves, wild and domestic, reflecting the enormous weight-bearing forces that concentrate over the MLHA, compressing and *melding* frog and heels together as though they were a single *contiguous* structure.

meld – to merge or blend as though welded together

contiguous – touching or connected throughout in an unbroken sequence

extremely important focus and area of practice in your **Cadaver Trim Clinic**. Both heels, in conjunction with the forward toe wall pillar established by H°TL, therefore, contribute definitively to natural hoof balance: mediolaterally (side to side) and anteroposteriorly (front to rear).

Natural hoof balance defined

Natural hoof balance is defined by a complex composite of well-defined, epidermal relationships located by the Navigational Landmarks: active and passive wear patterns, orientation of tubular horn, Healing Toe Length (H°TL), hard sole plane (HSP), hard frog plane (HFP), and heel balance (MLHA). While each part is complex in its own right, the basic natural trim guidelines provide a direct path to their individual resolutions culminating in comprehensive hoof balance.

Figure P5-8 provides a view to a balanced wild hoof from behind; **Figure P5-9** provides a volar view of a balanced domestic hoof.

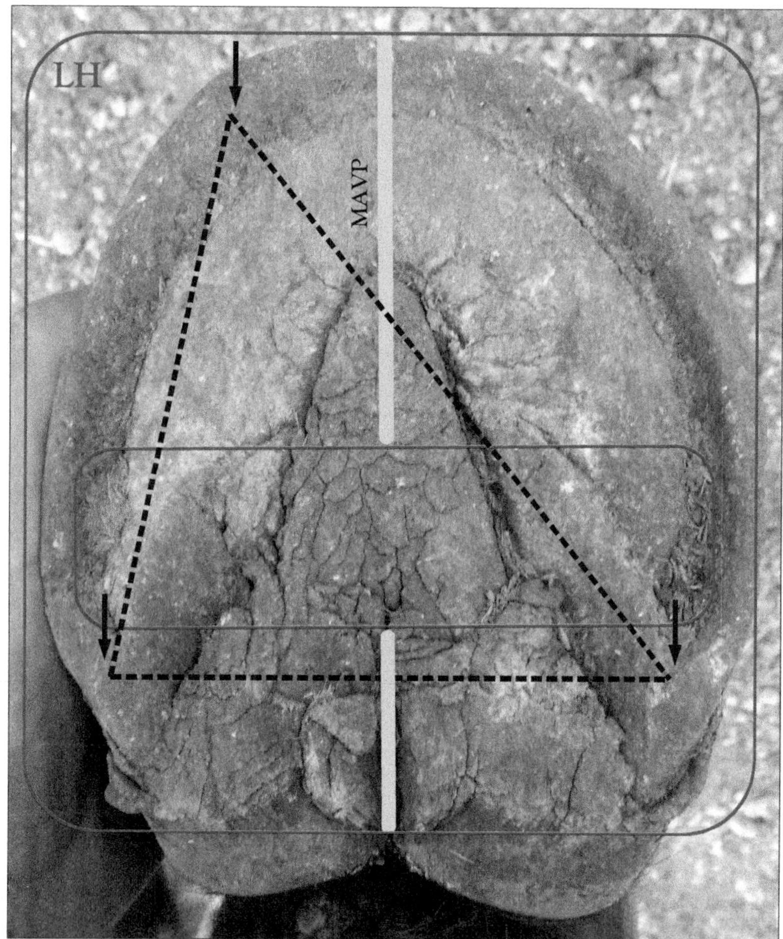

Figure P5-9 . *Hoof balance defined.* Grooved centerline of simulated *Hoof Balancer* is positioned over the MAVP of a naturally shaped, left hind hoof ready to be trimmed. *Black arrows* point to support pillars. *Dashed lines* articulate to define the *support triad.* A piece of paper will slide unobstructed under the Hoof Balancer anywhere between the support pillars along the hoof wall.

Study Assignment
Part 3 What is Hoof Balance?

PowerPoint Lecture: "Active and Passive Wear" – More clarification on how natural wear patterns "balance" the hoof capsule during support.

Step 1 – ISNHCP Training Program

Independent Study

Part 6 - Hoof Form and Function

The focus of this discussion will be somewhat varied, but with a central theme – what happens to the horse's foot in flight and support. Your reading assignment will be all of Chapter 7 in *The Natural Trim.*

Anthropomorphism – an interpretation of what is not human or personal in terms of human or personal characteristics

The chapter opens with a discussion of the horse's natural gaits, challenging the *anthropomorphic* assumption held by most of the horse world: the horse's movements are simply "gaits" that riders more or less contrive and exploit for their personal utility with no thought given to what they are relative to the horse's natural state. Contraposing this view is that the natural gaits are rooted in the *natural behaviors* of the horse, meaning horses are selected by nature to move in particular ways based on their adaptation. Certainly this doesn't mean just whatever humans want them to do. This ignorant disconnect from the horse's natural world – not really knowing how horses move naturally and why (behavior) – is arguably the leading cause of equestrian-based lameness among domesticated horses. Stated simply, horses are compelled to move in ways that nature never intended and with the result their bodies are broken down.

The chapter continues by revealing how this disconnect shows up specifically in hoof care based on bogus models of hoof function, known as the *hoof mechanism.* In my opinion, because these truly fail to explain what happens to the hoof during its flight and support phases in any way that reckons with the horse's natural world, the result – like disconnected horsemanship – is devastating to the horse's feet. For example, rationales for horseshoeing and invasive trimming methods ignore the foot's natural state. The NHC model departs from conventional thinking, and unifies natural hoof "form" and "function" based on the wild horse foot, and the specie's behavior-based "natural gait complex."[1] The widely successful application of the natural trim with domesticated horses, and the natural behavior-based move-

[1]An unpublished experiment called the "Strip Test" was conducted at the AANHCP Field Headquarters in 2010 to prove the NHC model for the mechanism. Thin strips of duct tape were tightly applied to the outer wall in various locations while sample hooves were held in hand or in support. Horses were then walked, trotted, and cantered down a gravel road. Convention states the "strips' should tear apart on the hoof if it were contracting and expanding according to their model. To a certain extent, common sense would also lead one to this conclusion, since a thousand pound animal pressing down on the hoof would argue for its expansion. But no strip was ripped or came loose during the test. The NHC model explains why.

ment witnessed by many in the Paddock Paradise of the AANHCP Field Headquarters and other such paddocks around the world, all testify to the accuracy and value of this model.

Study Assignment #1 – *The Natural Trim.* Jaime Jackson

- **Chapter 7: "Hoof Form and Function"** – Although I wrote this chapter six years ago, there's little to nothing I would change today. Read everything closely and be sure to study the NHC model for the hoof mechanism. Although counterintuitive in some respects, its logic follows from the premise that the lamellar leaves of the LAM are structurally too weak to support a thousand pound animal's weight (**p. 135**), but that the foot is equipped with a vast vascular "hydraulic" system supported by an abundance of flexible fibro-fatty *digital cushion*, and reciprocating tendons (DDFT and CDET) and their muscle groups that provide counter forces to the descending weight-bearing forces.

Study Assignment #2 – NHC Bulletin Series

- ***Bulletin #8: A New Theory: Time and Mass In A 4th-Dimensional Hoof Mechanism.* Jaime Jackson.** – Another view to the hoof mechanism written nine years before the *TNT* version.

PowerPoint Lecture: "The Hoof Mechanism" – I put this together four years after *TNT*. To date, I think this is my favorite characterization in terms of imagery.

Quiz (True or False)
Part 6 - Hoof Form and Function

1. The natural gaits aren't the same thing as the natural gait complex (NGC).
2. Wild mules can be part of family bands of horses.
3. Wild horse family bans occupy well-defined *home ranges.*
4. The NHC model for the hoof mechanism states that the "hoof lands, spreads apart a little under the weight of the horses, then springs back together again when the hoof leaves the ground."
5. Fluids in the foot's vascular channels under pressure from the weight-bearing force are said to be equalized by the presence of small "shunts" that open and close, connecting the sub-branches of the arteries and veins.
6. The NHC model for the hoof mechanism states that both P3 and the LAM are non-weight bearing structures during the hoof's support phase.

Step 1 – ISNHCP Training Program

Independent Study

Part 7 – Tools & Equipment

The ISNHCP specifies which tools and equipment will be used by the student during their training. It is well-known among professionals that poor quality tools and equipment preclude quality trimming. Hence, the ISNHCP makes this determination for students who are unlikely to know what is and isn't acceptable. Also, because many of the items that will be used are unique to the natural trim and not used by farriers, sources are limited; the ISNHCP website directs students to suppliers who carry these products.

Given the above, you are required to arrive with all required tools and equipment at each training session, beginning with your **Cadaver Trim Clinic**. Your clinicians will introduce you to their appropriate use and make sure that your trimming attire properly fits you. Visit the ISNHCP website's Student Store drop-down menu for a list of the required tools and equipment. The list below may not be current as new items can be added in at any time and others deleted.

Required Tools & Equipment

1. Tripod Hoof Stand-Work Center (WS-1 with Square Caddy is recommended)
2. G.E. Forge "Easy" 14-inch Standard and Race Track Hoof Nippers
3. F. Dick 14 inch Turf Rasp (shorter F. Dick rasps are not acceptable).
4. JV Brand 1.75" aluminum rasp handle (any color).
5. Halverson hoof knife (or F. Dick, your choice)
6. F. Dick hoof knife
7. Hoof Meter Reader (2 are required).
8. Hoof Balancer
9. Professional Hoof Pick (8 inch with formed handle)
10. Hoof Buffer (HB-1)
11. Hoof Buffer (HB-2)
12. Radius Rasp (RR-1)
13. Radius Rasp (RR-2)
14. Sole/Bar Rasp (SR-2)
15. Leather Apron (any color)

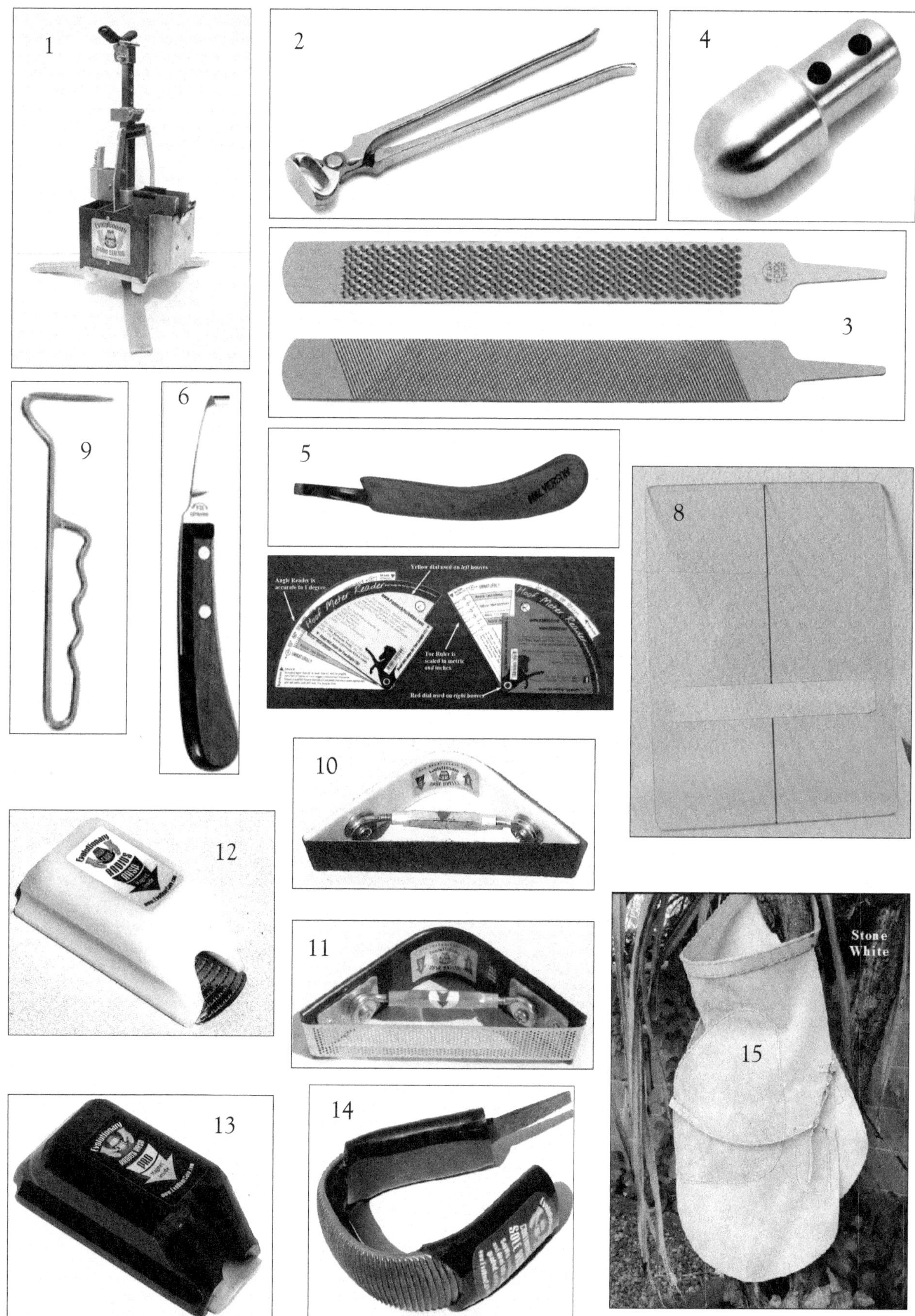
1
2
4
3
9
6
5
8
Angle Reader is accurate to 1 degree
Yellow dial used on left hooves
Hoof Meter Reader
Toe Ruler is scaled in metric and inches
Red dial used on right hooves
10
12
11
Stone White
15
13
14

Step 1 – ISNHCP Training Program

Independent Study Module

Part 8 – Physical Conditioning Exercises

Trimming horses requires that trimmers be in top physical and mental condition. This is necessary to prevent harm to yourself and the horse. So important is this facet of trimming that the ISNHCP requires students be in top shape if they are to proceed with training. The ISNHCP will not advance students past their **Sequencing Clinic** (discussed at length in **Part 9**, page 102 of this training manual) if it is clear that the exercises in this training manual have been ignored. Specific exercises are provided here as they will prepare your body for sequencing. Students who are insufficiently conditioned to sequence, will be required to undertaking additional physical training until evidence of strength and capability is confirmed by your **Sequencing** clinician *and* video submission to the ISNHCP. Students with medically diagnosed physical or mental disabilities should report this information to the ISNHCP before training commences. *Note that this caveat is included in the ISNHCP training application form.*

Because horses are by nature "animals of prey," they possess strong fear and flight instincts if subjected to strange, erratic or threatening behavior from their human handlers, spectators (including the owner), and anything in the environment that gives them concern. For this reason, the ISNHCP reserves the right to dismiss any student from the training program who arrives under the influence of behavior modifying drugs, including narcotics, alcohol, and cannabis products. Likewise, students exhibiting violent behavior towards the horse, towards students or towards instructors may also be expelled from the training program. Students with a medical history of drug addiction problems or anger management issues should report this to the ISNHCP prior to training. *The ISNHCP reserves the right to require legal drug testing or psychological evaluation of any student.*

Recommended exercises

Everyone has their personal ideas about exercising and being fit. My idea is to throw this notion of "I know how to exercise and be fit" right out the window when it comes to what we do under horses. The great body builder Arnold Alois Schwarzenegger once wrote that his wife asked him to hold their newborn baby in his arms, but that he couldn't hold the baby without tiring in only a fraction of the time of his wife. His message was that muscles have to be prepared for the type of work they are going to perform. Not to pick on Arnold, but he wouldn't last half the time he spent holding his baby when under a horse. Our work requires a specialized development of our muscles.

2017 marks my 70 years of age. I've been working under horses since the 1970s and here's some facts you are wise to consider and ponder. First, it is easier for me to trim today than when I was in my twenties. Unless the weather is very hot, I do not sweat, or very little at most; sweating is almost against my religion, meaning I'm not being very efficient. Most of the time, when I've finished trimming a horse, I feel like I've not done anything; it's really effortless work. In fact, I usually feel better afterwards. I swear, horses can heal. I never "rush" when doing my work. Watching me work, it would appear that I am not doing anything very fast. But I will complete most "maintenance" trims in less than 12 minutes of actual work time, sometimes just 8 minutes. 70 to 80 percent of the time that I am under the horse, I am actually taking a break *while working* – totally relaxed. If I can't relax, something is wrong. Horses understand one thing while I'm working with them – they are going to cooperate, and there is no way out of it. Horses understand one other thing – and this is why horses come to me to be trimmed, even fight with each other to be the first to be trimmed – I am going to protect, praise, and reward them. Horses immediately sense something different about me – what that "is" is what I learned from wild horses and they know it's a part of me. Horses and I also understand together – we much, much prefer that their owner or trainer not be present or within sight. Most clients I've served don't realize it, but I have a better relationship with their horses than they do. It's a fact.

But none of the above would be possible if I didn't exercise the way I do. Physical conditioning exercises are the "Golden Rule" to follow if you expect to trim horses into your 70s, 80s, and 90s without pain. If you think you're going to muscle your way through this, you will regret it one day with back pain and probably back surgery. Or you'll just give up, like Arnold!

I consider myself an expert at exercising. My expertise began when I was a teenager with *Osgood–Schlatter disease* – a painful inflammation in the knee area that occurs during young adolescence. The doctor took me out of regular "PE" at school, and I was put in what was derisively called the "ortho squad" by "normal" students. There were about 12 of us – all suffering from either congenital issues or temporary inflammations that prevented us from walking or functioning like everyone else. Several suffered from things like polio and heart ailments, and life for them would always be a struggle. I felt compassion for them, and even inspiration as they did whatever the gym teacher, Mr. Stratton, could facilitate. In addition to my knee problems, I wasn't doing too well on other fronts either. A really pretty girl I knew, whose attentions were much sought after by other boys, and who, for reasons I could never understand, always wanted to walk to and from school with me, even though she ridiculed me one day in front of others, "Jaime, you have no brains nor brawn." But the fact is, she was right. I was even flunking the 8th grade. Plus, being condemned to ortho didn't help any. I think Stratton, a WWII marine as I recall, saw my despair and, on the first day, he said, "Jaime, you are going to work with the 'weights' and exercises that you can do." I had no choice but to submit.

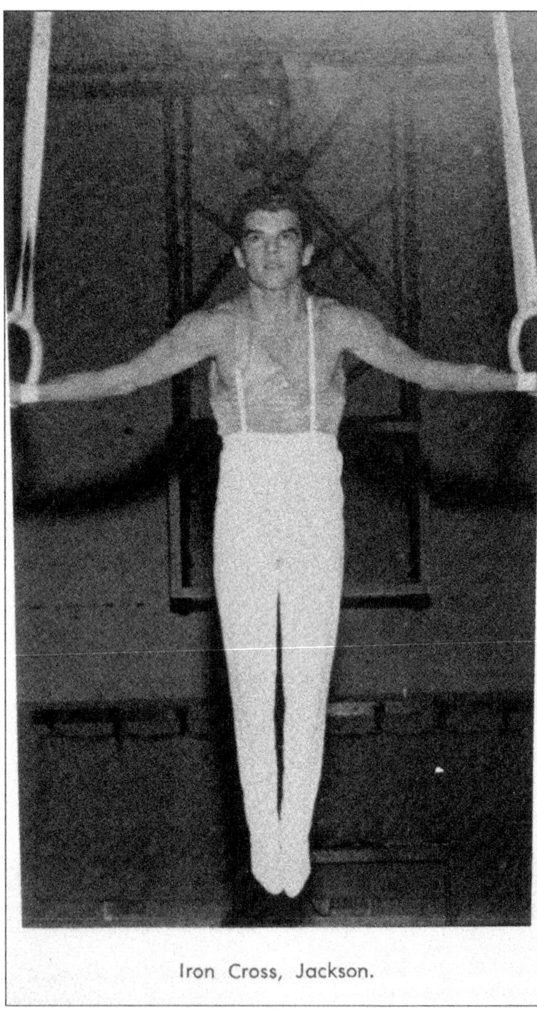
Iron Cross, Jackson.

What he put me through became the foundation I use pretty much to this date, with some adaptations. By the end of the school year, everyone I knew began to notice that I was looking different. Then one day, in the boy's locker room, where there was this giant white billboard with neatly printed black lettering that listed all the school's athletic records, my name was added for setting the school records for push-ups and chin-ups. This brought me to the attention of the school's gymnastics' team coach, Mr. Romo, and also the nearby high school's coach, Mr. Bellmar. I never returned to regular PE, but was shunted into competitive gymnastics where I excelled in the 20 ft. rope climb event, and won medals as a ring man. I am forever indebted to this string of teachers who taught me how to develop my body, and later, fellow gymnasts who with similar training, inspired me to learn what they had achieved.

It's my hope that you too will be inspired to condition yourself for our work with horses. There are fundamental exercises that you can do that will prepare your muscles for the specialized development they will go through under the horse. They will prepare you first for sequencing, and later for trimming. If you do not exercise, you will probably fail in this work, or at least be miserable every time you get under a horse. And you may hurt yourself. You are dealing with a thousand pound animal who is stronger than any of us, and if you aren't in shape, he will know it and probably exploit your weakness to his advantage. Horses are like that, for it is in their species's DNA.

20 minute exercise routine

I'm going to tell you what I do to keep in excellent shape, 5-6 days a week, first thing every morning for no more than 20 minutes. I've been doing these for so many decades I can't remember exactly when I developed them for our type of work. But they are foundational and I started doing them in some form when I was around 14 years old as an "ortho." You'll need some *dumbbells* and *hand grips* and a space no bigger than 8 ft. x 8 ft. You don't need to go to a gym for any of this. Your body and mind becomes your gym.

It all starts with the concept of *progressive development.* In a previous version of this training manual I explained what this is:

> The following are daily exercises; typically, they are grouped in "sets". Each set includes "repetitions" (reps) of the particular exercise. On non-trimming days (days off from your work), we do multiple sets; on trimming days, we may or may not do fewer sets. It is also important to take days off to rest your body, during which no exercises are recommended. Here's why: multiple sets gradually develop the muscles of your body for hard work (like trimming horses). At first, you will do fewer reps; but as the weeks and months go by, you will automatically be able to increase the number you can do. I call this "progressive development". It applies equally to your trimming. At first, you will only be able to do a few hooves at a time, maybe only one hoof. Then, through progressive development, you will be able to do two hooves without stopping, then three, and, one day, the entire horse! Also, at first, your mind will be saying, "I can't do this". But, once more, through progressive development, your unconscious mind will begin to "take over" and say, "Now I can do this".

Stretching

This is such an individualized thing to do, so everyone will have to figure this one out for themselves. I personally do mine standing up, bending this way and that depending on how I feel. I don't spend much time doing it either, probably less than 2 minutes, as my exercises really do 99% of it for me.

Push-ups

This is truly the great muscle builder that covers the entire body (*above, facing page*). Some very impressive athletes do nothing but push-ups for their exercising. World records are astonishing, in the tens of thousands non-stop! Some record holders do them on the backs of their hands! Others using just one arm. Some just one finger! The most knuckle push-ups in one hour by a woman is 1,206 by Eva Clarke (Australia) on 31 January 2014! Whoa! We won't go to such extremes, and I do hope these competitors aren't using steroids? I think a good number to shoot for is 100 push-ups in five sets of 20, spread out between the other exercises. You'll find that the sets get easier as time goes by as muscle mass develops and conditions. It's amazing what the human body can do, when we try.

You will probably feel "muscle burn" as you fatigue. This is due to glucose breakdown by the body resulting in lactic acidosis (the chemistry is complex[1]). If this occurs, simply stop, walk around or stretch a moment, rest, and then resume. It's perfectly natural and nature is just warning you to rest a few moments before continuing; when the burn subsides, continue. It happened to me all the time as a gymnast and happens to me everyday that I exercise as I reach my self-imposed limits. No big deal! Also, as with any compression exercise, breathe in as you let yourself down, and blow out as you push upwards; whatever, just get enough oxygen to continue. Shoot for one push-up per second.

If you can't do a push-up with your body levered straight from head to toe, do them on your knees. If you can only do one or two, that's where you start. Over time, possibly many months, you will eventually graduate to knees off the ground. Obviously, you can't do a hundred at the onset (i.e., 5 sets of 20), so your goal will

[1] $C_6H_{12}O_6 \rightarrow 2\ CH_3COCO_2^- + 2\ H^+$

There are many variations of the push-up, one of the great "compression" based exercises for muscle development. Find your way to one or more of them. At age 70, I do 100 as part of my 20 minutes exercise regimen, but am conditioned to do 1,000 in about 8 hours. Here I am at 17 doing a push-up and "hold" with my legs off the ground on my way to a handstand – no steroids either! If you're new to the push-up, they're tough at first, but incredibly easy later if you follow the principle of *progressive development* – the key also to effortless trimming. You can do it!

be whatever you are capable of doing over your 20 minute regime. I do 20 in about 20 seconds (50/minute) – the world record is 134/minute done on the back of the hands!

So, do your push-ups in sets of whatever you are able to achieve at first, on your knees if needed. If you simply can't do push-ups but on your knees, that's okay, do them like that because it's still very effective. According to a study published in the Journal of Strength and Conditioning Research, the test subjects supported with their hands, on average, 69.16% of their body mass in the up position, and 75.04% in the down position during the traditional push-ups. In modified push-ups, where knees are used as the pivot point, subjects supported 53.56% and 61.80% of their body mass in up and down positions, respectively.[1] Nature will let you know eventually if you can do them levered (hands only). If 100 proves to be beyond your reach (five sets of 20 = 100/20 minutes), then pick a lower number and set that as a goal (e.g., five sets of 8 = 40/20 min). I remember when I did 50 years ago, and now I am at 100/20 min, although over a larger period of time, 5 hours, I'm fairly confident I can do 1,000. It gets that easy, just like trimming horses gets easier and easier when you exercise following the principle of progressive development.

Squats

Another great exercise, I do only one set of ten and I stop bending before my thighs are parallel with my knees. Some experts claim my "high squats" (instead of low – below the parallel) put the lumber spine and knees at risk of injury over the long term. Well, at 50 plus years of doing them this way, I concur with other trainers who believe that high squats are one of the best exercises for developing muscles and strength. Likely, the problems occurred because of adding heavy (barbell) weights to the exercise and overloading the body. But since we don't do that, and there's no need to, our squats are perfectly safe. My "rule" is to always have my feet in view during the squat and keep my thighs higher than my knees. Also, keep your heels always at shoulder width – which we will integrate with sequencing later.

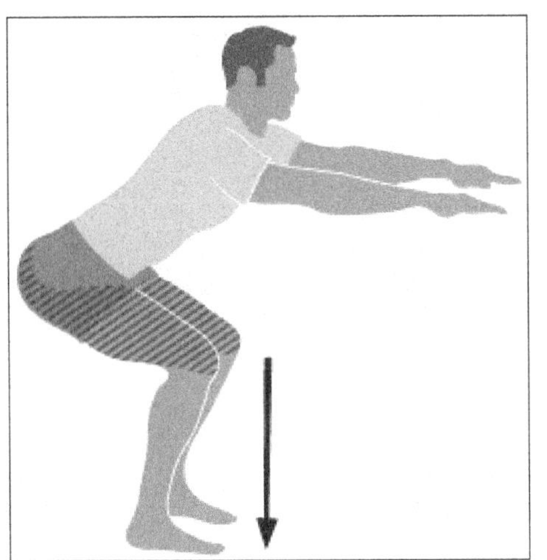

[1]Suprak, David N; Dawes, Jay; Stephenson, Mark D (February 2011). "The Effect of Position on the Percentage of Body Mass Supported During Traditional and Modified Push-up Variants". Journal of Strength and Conditioning Research. 25 (2): 497–503. doi:10.1519/JSC.0b013e3181bde2cf.

I conclude my squat set by holding the final one for 60 seconds (or until lactosis forces me up!). I do this by bracing both of my forearms near the elbows on my thighs just above the knees; I usually alternate by substituting one or both hands. I call this the "deep and low" position during trimming, and I use the heck out of it whenever I can which is most of the time. Students are doing this in the photo on page 105 of this manual. Once your body is conditioned through all of these exercises, you'll be able to go deep and low to take breaks while under the horse.

The squat also prepares us to lift our tools/equipment with our powerful hip and leg muscles, rather than bending over at the waist to lift which is a sure way to injure your lower back (sciatica). So, squats are a very important part of your training because we use it on every hoof. And the good news is that by going deep and low with the squat, we are afforded rest time under the horse without having to leave the horse to take a break and recover. Moreover, a good deal of our trimming can be done efficiently and safely by going deep and low. Learning to relax under the horse sends a message to the horse to relax and that all is in good order. Notice in the photo several pages back that I'm slightly smiling during the "Iron Cross" on the still rings. Same thing, I'm actually pretty relaxed — and I was required by the rules to hold it for 4 to 5 seconds. During some routines, I would transform the cross into variations and sustain the position for 8 to 12 seconds. Again, I couldn't do that at the beginning, but with progressive development I could.

Sit-ups

Like push-ups and squats, there's many ways to do these. My preference is to lay on my back with knees drawn up and hands clasped behind my neck, then simply tighten my stomach muscles, but always keeping flat on my back (*below*). At one point I was doing 400, but that turned out to be an unnecessary number of reps. I

Jack LaLanne – one of my exercise heroes!

do 50 now and that does it for my purposes.

I complete the sit-up exercises by balancing myself on my hips like the late famous exercise aficionado Jack LaLanne and his wife Elaine are demonstrating above. I've included a second stretching exercise featuring LaLanne which is also part of my warm-up exercise routine ("Stretching"). LaLanne and his wife lived just north of Lompoc in Moro Bay, before he passed away at age 96 in 2011. (Interesting family note: my Uncle George, who never exercised, passed away just a couple of years ago at age 101!). LaLanne did amazing feats of strength, including 1,033 push-ups in 23 minutes at age 42 on TV in 1956! In 1984, at age 70 – handcuffed, shackled, and fighting strong winds and currents – he towed 70 rowboats, one with several persons aboard, one mile across the Long Beach Harbor in Southern California! Holy smokes! Not surprising, LaLanne was an inspiration to a young Arnold Schwarzenegger just arrived in the U.S. from Austria.

Hand grippers

I use these hand instruments primarily to simulate nipper work. Some have adjustable spring tensioners, though I just use the $5 Wal-Mart gripper which works fine (*facing page*). Make sure the tension spring is something you can readily squeeze or you'll be complaining of *carpal tunnel syndrome* before long. I do fifty reps alternating squeezes between my left and right hands, then both hands simultaneously – all the while doing squats (my way of increasing the number of squat reps but spreading them out over the entire workout). When I'm done with these

Hand grippers — many to choose from, and I would find one that falls within your grip strength. This is an important exercise tool for working the nippers. The stronger your grip, the easier it will be to cut through tough hoof wall.

1

2

3

50 reps, I finish up in the deep and low position, where I count to 60 (one minute) while lightly touching the fingertips of my left and right hands together, one by one in sequence (left little finger to right little finger, left ring finger to right ring finger, etc.). This tactile concentration brings me into a deep, Zen like focus, which I often enter into when trimming. This helps me to connect the eye to the nipper to the hoof, thereby facilitating an efficient precision cut. This is highly important if you intend to enter the Advance Natural Trim course, where I expect cuts to be made with millimetric accuracy – necessary if one is to communicate effectively with the Healing Field via the epidermal medulla channeling energy to the nerve bed (**Part 2 – Structures of the horse's foot**).

Dumbbells

This is the last group of exercises I do. Their purpose is to strengthen and condition the arm, shoulder, and chest muscles for nippering and carrying the hoof stand about. They really give you that "cut" look, too! The first question is, what weight dumbbell does one use? The rule I go by is select the maximum weight you can comfortably and safely control through an entire set of reps. Let's follow along with the images across the top of the pages.

#1 demonstrates the alternating bicep curl; #2, the two arm curl. Notice that both subjects have their wrist/palms facing forward in the pre-lift, lower position. This is the most common position one sees people using in the gyms. *My advice is not to use it.* Here's why: without holding the weights, let both of your arms and hands hang down at rest. You'll notice that your palms are facing towards your

4

body and slightly rearward. This is their natural hanging position. Now raise them so that your palms are facing towards your body as the two subjects are doing. Lower them back down. You'll notice that as you raise and lower your arms, they rotate away from and towards their resting positions. This is exactly the rotation I used pressing to a handstand on the rings in the earlier photo – and I was lifting and pressing a heck of a lot more weight than any of us are going to do with weights. Arnold wrote in one of his books that he didn't like using machines because they cramped the natural movements of his body, including his hands and arms. So, when using the dumbbells be sure to follow as much as possible their natural trajectories and Arnold's warning.

Okay, go back to your basic push-up position and notice how you naturally position your hands on the floor. You'll probably find them rotated slightly inward, depending on your unique conformation. If so, that's your starting and ending position. It should feel natural and comfortable. If you're feeling any undue torsion (twist) on your wrists, you've not found your natural position. Now, go back and look at my wrist position in the floor exercise photo – try to figure that out! As I complete my press to the handstand, my wrists began to rotate until I'm back at the basic push-up hand position (from which I started). All this detail I had to scrutinize in order to do these power moves, but in each instance I was seeking out my natural hand, arm and body positions and their corresponding trajectories. One doesn't just do these things, one figures it out. Believe me, you'll be doing that with your clinician's guidance during sequencing. And, I would add, your overall sense of balance is also germane – meaning finding your *center of gravity*. A big, big topic during sequencing! But you'll do great because you're going to start exercising ASAP!

Moving to photo #3, the subject is in a good resting position and proceeds to press the dumbbells, alternating left and right. Again, examine any tendency for your wrist to rotate and follow that movement – do this first, without the dumbbell, to confirm. I do 20 alternate reps. Before I do two arm presses, I switch to #4 doing 10 reps, which adds further dimension to upper body strength and muscle definition, but without fatiguing the muscle groups used in #3. Back to #3, I'll do 16 two arm presses, then finish up with #4.

This brings us to #5, which I used to develop my chest muscles for the still rings, facilitating the Iron Cross and other power moves. Turns out it is useful too for our work. But careful with this exercise! Notice that the subject is doing this on a bench with bent arms. I do mine on the floor – less chance of the dumbbells pulling my arms down out of control. Bending the arms contributes to the pulling inward action as you raise the dumbbells and straighten your arms to the resting position. You can do this straight arm too, as I do from habit as a gymnast, but you should build strength to do this or you can hurt your shoulder joints. Again, if you start with a weight that you can control, and do fewer reps to begin, you won't have a problem. When doing the lift (press) tighten your stomach muscles to aid in the work. I do two sets of 10 lifts, with a short break in between sets. This is a great power builder, but stay within your body's limits.

I finish by doing 40 push-ups, which, you may find as a surprise, are easier to do than the first set of half that number. I'm conditioned to do 100 consecutive push-ups, but my routine is designed to develop the muscles for shorter work spans, which is more in sync for ring work and, relevant here, working under the horse. I met a woman years ago who could bend a thick iron horseshoe with her "gloved" hands – her chest muscles being the "key" to doing this. This can also be achieved by about 30% of our fellow (gifted) human beings through what I call "deep rapport" concentration, which I teach in the Advanced Trim Guidelines Training Program to help facilitate mass changes in the "Healing Field" when we are facing "deep pathology."

Summary

In all of these exercises, I don't stop to take lengthy breaks, only long enough to sip water, a few seconds, which I do throughout the routine — and as I do with trimming horses. So, it's pretty much non-stop. Jack LaLanne advocated for the continuous (non-stop), fluid integration of exercises, which I obviously fully embrace.

I listen to New Age music to go with my work flow, as it helps mitigate any mental or environmental noise that might disturb the routine and my deeper mental purpose to heal horses. Trimming for me is a Zen — meditative — experience, as it should be, because, by definition, H° invites our deepest understanding that "all things are connected" and we are healing an animal contending with the pernicious forces of domestication.

Your study assignment is to move quickly to create your 20 minute exercise regimen. This is as much for the horses you will face, as it is for yourself. You will do great!

Now, on to *sequencing*, a strategically important door into the horse's natural world . . . .

Step 1 – ISNHCP Training Program

Independent Study

Part 9 - Sequencing

The whole point of **Part 8 – Physical Conditioning Exercises** was to prepare you for *sequencing*. Sequencing is a holistic approach to trimming the horse based on the following integrated foundation:

- Efficient tool and equipment management.
- Communication with the horse through *relative dominance* (RD).
- Optimal positioning of trimmer, handler and horse.

Sequencing evolved out of the convergence of three *disparate* experiences in my life: my work as a professional farrier, my training as a competitive gymnast, and my wild horse studies. What I learned from wild horses gave me the insights to keep or discard what I learned from some truly talented farriers, both at the hoof and in terms of horse handling. From gymnastics came the personal discipline and knowledge of how to be strong, athletic, and healthy. From the wild horse came a keen understanding of natural equine behavior. The wild horse was the actual catalyst that enabled me to synthesize all three experiences into what I defined and later taught as sequencing.

disparate – different from each other

As a farrier, I paid attention to what a number of professional farriers were doing. I worked side by side with three, whom I greatly respected. I also read about the history of the farrier sciences and attended farrier conventions. Later, I spoke at the 1988 Annual Conference of the American Farriers Association about my wild horse studies. Truly professional farriers are rare, as the landscape has filled with poorly trained "backyard" shoers and barefooters. Of the many I met, mostly men, I found to be gentlemen, helpful and even selfless, talented, and respectful. Even as a "renegade" NHC practitioner, I do not hold any hostility towards my old profession. A large part of what they are is still a part of me, and that will always be the case. And of that part, I have brought into sequencing, including some body positioning, some of the tools and equipment, and even some of the horse handling skills I was taught.

From gymnastics came the athleticism I still enjoy today, and which I discussed in the previous discussion (**Part 8**). The self-discipline and basic techniques I learned have never left me, and they have integrated perfectly into sequencing. Per-

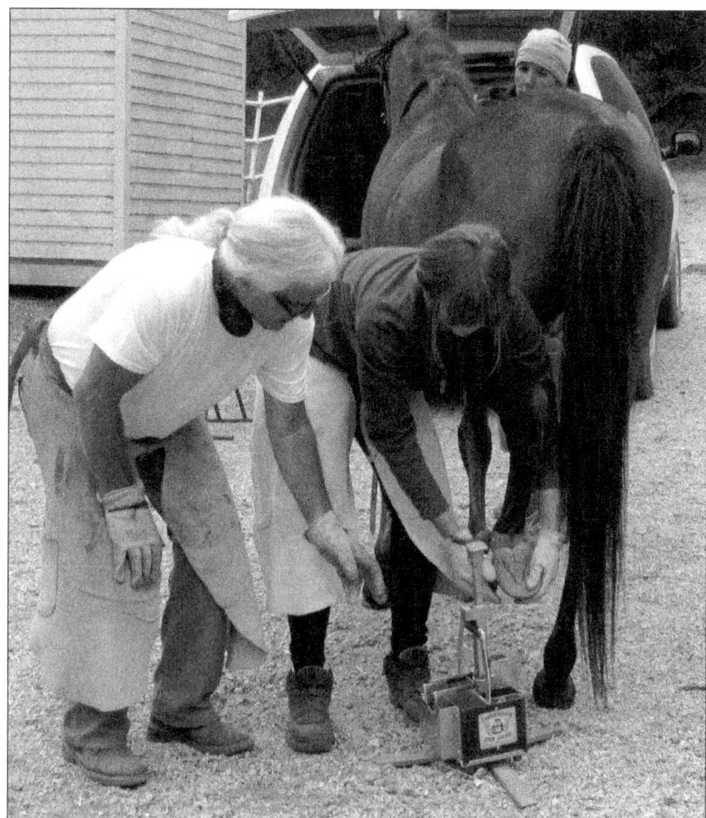

General Jackson counsels his student. "Why, you're not in 'deep and low!' Bend those legs! Relax your back! Heels at shoulder width! Lower that grip head! What's it doin' up there? Guide that hoof – don't lift it! This is boot camp, not pretend time!"

haps most important from that experience came the appreciation of *progressive development* and the patience and hard work that goes with it. It is the true road to good health and a positive attitude towards life. Believe me, we need both to deal with a very troubled horse world!

The wild horse brought yet another dimension to the work table. For me, they eliminated any pretense about who I am as a person or the inherent value of what I am trying to do for their species based on their natural world. The horse world is full of gossip, unrestrained egos that hunger to feed the self even at the willful expense of the horse, ignorance, violence, neglect, and denial. Not that there aren't good things happening, especially as a result of the NHC revolution, it's just that not nearly enough is happening when horsemanship is held to the light of nature.

At the hoof, I learned that we – as professional farriers – have had it basically all wrong. The suggestion, for example, that shoeing is a "necessary evil," is simply bogus. No one has to do anything with horses that would require shoes. In fact, horses are no longer a necessity in a modern world. They are holdovers from a previous era. So, if we are going to own them today, so my rationale has been since I entered their natural world, then we ought to do it right by them. Unfortunately, old traditions die hard and Hollywood movies haven't helped. Tons of people still enter the horse world wanting to look and ride like mythical cowboys created in movies and on TV. Just nonsense that horses pay dearly for.

The wild horse gave me the "ammunition" to fight back for their cause to have dignity in a world rife with anthropomorphism that insists they are not horses, but mere extensions of human fantasies with which to have fun. I drew my own battle lines in the dirt, and invited the fight. It's been an easy one for me, however, because the wild horse gave me their truth and I can live with it in the best of spirits as I do my work. Admittedly, the farriers have turned their backs on this, but, at the same time, I've probably not done the best job in trying to reach across to them. I'll try harder in the future.

But it has been horse owners, and largely women, who have truly risen to the occasion. Given their enthusiasm, I made the decision years ago to train them in the horse's natural world of NHC. But even here, it was not original thought of my own to do so. One of the farriers I learned from, Bob Peters (from Chicago), who was of my parent's generation and now passed away, trained women to shoe. "You can do it," he told female horse owners. And I watched him do it, and, we all actually had a lot of fun "turning heads" shoeing horses side by side in barns and at ranches where, traditionally back then, only men did such work. Bob understood progressive development, too, and enforced the rule – gruffly so at times – "You don't get to do this, until you first learn to do that."

Back in those days, too, hoof stands we know today didn't exist. The one we use in the ISNHCP training program is very sophisticated, and Bob would probably be amazed. At the same time, he would probably be amazed at how we trim the hooves. Bob learned to be a farrier himself from a man of an earlier generation who shod two horses a day when he was over 90! He in turn learned from professional blacksmiths that continued back into the old European traditions brought to America hundreds of years ago. That which enabled that man to do what he was doing at that advanced age was passed to Bob and then to me, and I'm passing it along to you today embedded in sequencing. No doubt, if you finish this course, you too will pass it along, long after I have gone on to walk among the stars.

Missing from my training as a farrier, and as a gymnast, was the horse's natural social order taught to me by wild horses. There, the entire truth came out. The

"Get down there — it's 'deep and low' again. Do you feel the 'burn' yet? No, then stay down there! Mommy's not coming to save you. Why are you smiling? I want burning muscle. Tighten those stomach muscles. Very good! Now relax them. What do think this is, play day? This is boot camp!"

more I learned from them, the harder and harder it became to be conversant with people about horse behavior. This included equestrian "experts." I even challenged a distinguished rider from the Spanish Riding School, telling him that not one rider in their quadrille was even remotely sitting naturally on their horses, nor was the hoof work even remotely "humane." To my surprise, he agreed! There's a whole lot more to that story I've not gone public with.

But back to sequencing. In large part, it is about understanding the horse and what we must do to partner with them as their "senior" in the horse's natural "pecking order." It's been my observation of the many strains of horsemanship, from cowboys stuff, to the highest levels of dressage, to backyard horsemanship, to you name it, the meaning of pecking order or "dominance" training is simply polluted nonsense with the horse a victim. As part of NHC, pecking order translates to "relative dominance," or RD for short. Once properly understood — and there are no guarantees — another world opens up to you. The "gate locks" keeping you out are personal ego, equestrian traditions, "authorities," and a genuine lack of interest in natural behavior.

I have seen less than a half dozen truly "natural horsemen" in my nearly half a century of doing this. All have one thing in common — no one's ever heard of them. None of them have written books — one was the grandson of a slave here in the U.S. who could neither read nor write. Generally, however, people do notice something about their riding that is different, but simply misunderstand as to what it is exactly. I know there are others out there, but finding them would be difficult except through chance. The popular riding programs people see advertised do not include radar that would lead to these unknowns. Typically, they are pragmatists who are uncannily perceptive and intuitive. They may show up in competitions, but not in the usual way. For example, one is a bullfighter in Spain. All share the common trait of expecting precision in their work with horses, but it is not forced. All can ride without reins, spurs, or saddles, which the rest of the horse world clings to for control. I know of one dog trainer (pointed out to me via his TV program by my colleague Jill Willis) who would understand what I'm talking about because he relates to the dog's nature the same way that I do to horses. Although the dog is a natural predator and the horse is a natural prey animal, it is fascinating how the laws of nature pass through each species in very similar ways.

Assignments

Two things I want you to do: the reading and video assignments below, and then try sequencing yourself. No trimming, just sequencing. Then create a video of yourself sequencing according to the assignments and submit it to your **Sequencing** clinician for feedback before you attend their clinic. Our clinicians will be expecting this from you. The purpose is to get you somewhat ready so that your clinician can help you refine your technique once you attend the sequencing clinic. Why wait around doing nothing in the meantime? This will facilitate you moving forward with your training sooner than if you were to do nothing but the required exercises. Experience has taught us that motivated students can do this preliminary work on their own. Of course, if you're simply having too many problems on your own, you might need to wait until you take the **Sequencing Clinic**. If this is the case, and I imagine it won't be in most cases unless you are simply lazy by nature, which I can't imagine if you're wanting to do this kind of work in the first place, then just do the exercises. The video you are going to send to your **Sequencing** clinician will tell them if you are doing just fine, have a real problem needing a clinic to solve, or are simply *indolent*.

indolent – showing an inclination to laziness

Study Assignment #1 – *The Natural Trim: Principles and Practice.* Jaime Jackson

- **Introduction to Part 2: "Readying Ourselves to Trim," pp. 159-175** – This material is a little dated – the hoof stand has evolved further, plus there are newly invented tools. But the sections on RD, treating, and body positioning are relevant and critical.

Study Assignment #2 – Power Point Lectures

– Both of these assignments are critical and expand on the *TNT* discussions in the above assignment.

- **Power Point Lecture: "RD and working with horses"**
- **Power Point Lecture: "Sequencing step-by-step"**

Quiz (True or False)
Part 9 – Sequencing

1. Treating is important to reinforce cooperative behavior with the horse.
2. Ear radar can tell us where the horse's attentions are.
3. Tail swishing can be a sign the horses is irritated with us.
4. Free-reining is a way to trim the horse without a handler.
5. The diagonal is a significant part of the horse's natural support position
6. When setting the diagonal pressure is applied to the horse's shoulder and may be supported by lead line pressure on the same side.
7. The horse will move backwards each time we set his diagonal.
8. The grip head will slope down in the direction of the toe.
9. Light pressure to the horse's stomach muscles tends to lighten and raise the fore-limb.
10. Kneeling to trim the hind limb is a violation of sequencing protocol.
11. The correct position of the horse's hind limb above the hock joint is under the trimmer's arm pit during trimming.
12. The MATW is set against the cradle when trimming the hind hoof.
13. Treating and/or praising the horse after every act of cooperation encourages negative behavior.
14. Treating and/or praising the horse at any time does not encourage negative behavior.
15. Setting the diagonal, turns on the hindquarters, turns on the forehand, and side passes are the most direct and efficient ways to position a horse for trimming.

Step 1 – ISNHCP Training Program

Independent Study

Part 10 – The Natural Trim Step-by-Step

The trim guidelines for the basic natural trim are relatively straight forward when applied to hooves not suffering from extreme capsule deformity. Since it is the objective of this training program to teach natural trim "basics," instruction does not include deformed hooves suffering the effects of chronic, deep pathology exacerbated by neglect, bogus science, and gross incompetence. Students who successfully complete this basics course will have the opportunity to apply to the Advanced Natural Trim Training Program.

Below is a brief description of the steps involved in the basic natural trim, including reference to required study materials and quizzes. Other than the Step 1 gathering of the Critical Measurements below, there are no practical assignments here for you to do. From Step 2 below onward, each practicum you will do under the direct guidance of your **Cadaver Trim** clinician. *Experimenting on your own horse is not advised as you can cause harm.*

In this section of the training manual, I'm going to recommend two assignments with which to augment the following description of the natural trim. Once more, time has passed since both educational materials were created – new tools/equipment, and techniques. Your job is to exercise critical thinking in your evaluations of what we did 5 years ago, versus what we do today in the discussion below.

Assignment #1: PowerPoint Lecture – "Natural Trim Step-by-Step"

Assignment #2: *The Natural Trim* – Chapter 8 "Trimming the Biodynamically Balanced Hoof."

Step 1: Measuring and recording data (pre-trim)

Grid-lining the hoof with the Navigational Landmarks and then collecting the Critical Measurements is the first step. The measurement data tells us "where the hoof is at" relative to the wild horse model, and "where we are heading" with the trimming. As you become more and more proficient at measuring and trimming, contrasting pre-trim with post-trim information, particularly over the long term, will begin to resonate in terms of understanding stability in H° and H°TL and what they mean in terms of the foot's vitality. As NHC practitioners our objective

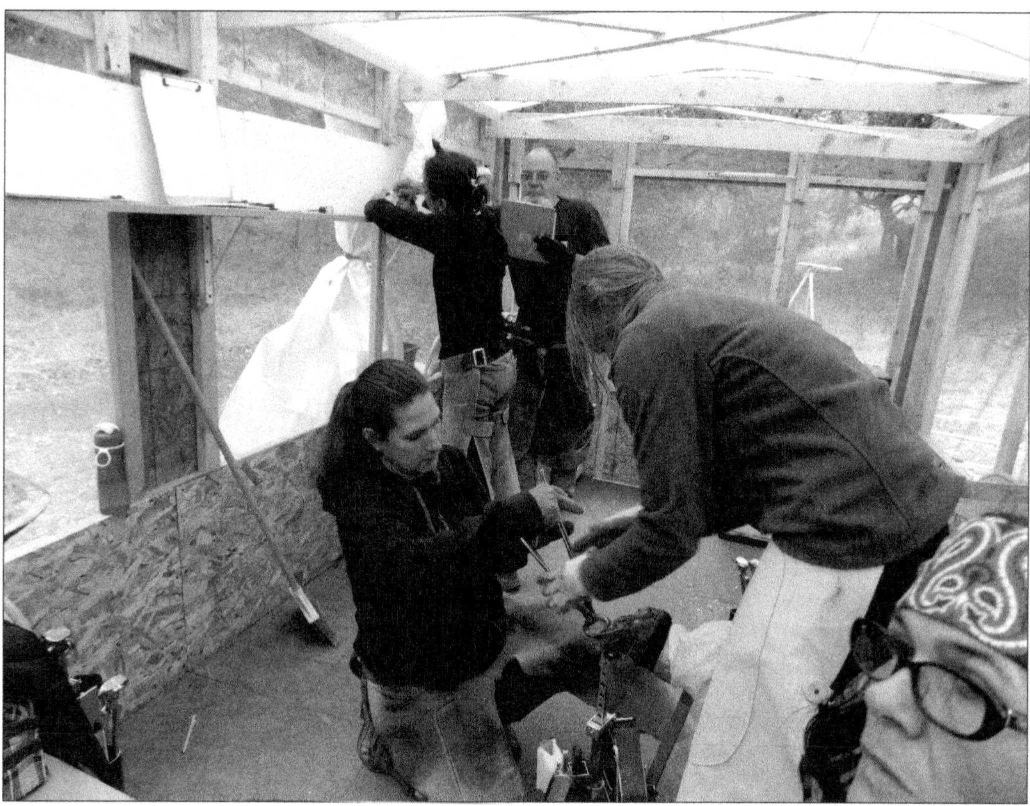

Clinicians help students one-on-one in a cadaver trim clinic.

is always soundness and health, and these Critical Measurements are our greatest allies in making that determination.

In this clinic you will be measuring and recording data for each cadaver hoof you trim, using the same guidelines and data form I introduced you to in **"Part 3 – Importance of Measuring"** of this training manual. As I wrote then, practice on your own or friends' horses (but without trimming them). Bring with you to the clinic a dozen or more data forms copied from the pdf provided in the DVD you received. Keep these in a binder. Later you will add other data forms from the **Live Horse Trim Clinic** and **mentorships, case studies**, and all **final field exams**. If you think you're going to apply to the Advanced Trim Training Program, I will probably ask to see these data forms.

Step 2: Nipper dragging to find the Hard Sole Plane (HSP)

The hoof nipper is the principal tool used in Step 2. Nipper dragging [**Figure P5-4**] enables us to expose the HSP, determine H°TL, locate the forward most support pillar of the VP Triad [**Figure P5-2**], and, ultimately, establish natural "hoof balance." Significant, unnatural irregularities in the surface of the sole not remov-

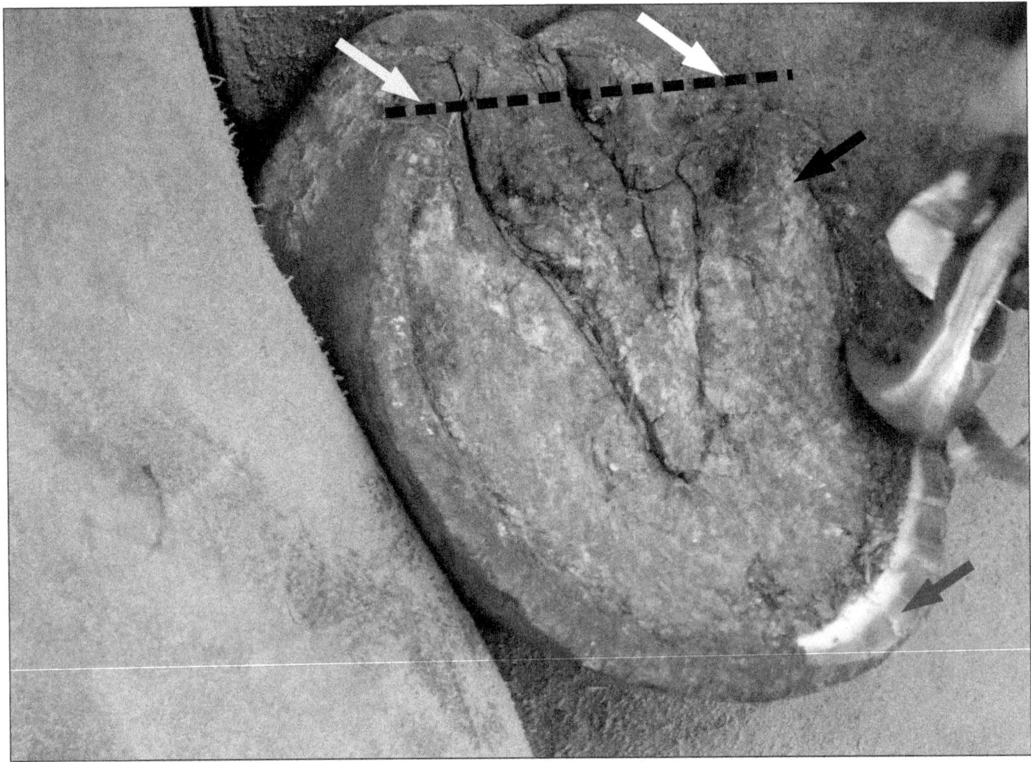

[**Figure S4**] *Blue arrow* points to thickened medial toe wall, the forward pillar of the emerging support triad. *White arrow* points to back of the medial heel, location of the second pillar of the triad. *Black arrow* points to HSP of medial seat-of-corn – my navigational guide into the heel-buttress. I am midway in my nipper run between these two triad support pillars. *Dashed line* marks the MLHA. *Yellow arrow* points to impending location of lateral heel support pillar. Many years of experience, coupled to a naturally worn hoof of one of our AANHCP horses, have enabled me to sight each support pillar without marking the Navigational Landmarks. But hooves suffering from extreme pathology or extreme overgrowth due to criminal neglect will be gridded.

able through nipper dragging, are removed using either the *hoof knife* or *SR-2* (sole rasp), or both if need be.

Step 3: Balancing the heels with the "Heel Balancer"

Balancing the heels [**Figures P5-6 thru 5-9**] and shortening them to their natural length, completes the VP Triad and renders hoof balance, the main objective of the natural trim.

Step 4: Trimming the hoof wall relative to the HSP

With H°TL shortened to the HSP, and the heels balanced and trimmed to their natural length, the hoof is now balanced. With this step, the stretches of hoof wall between the VP Support Triad are shortened to the HSP [**Figure S4** and **Figures S5a-e**]. Of course, the diagrammatic is only an abstract representation to you at this point in time, but it will "come to life" in the clinic as you draw and

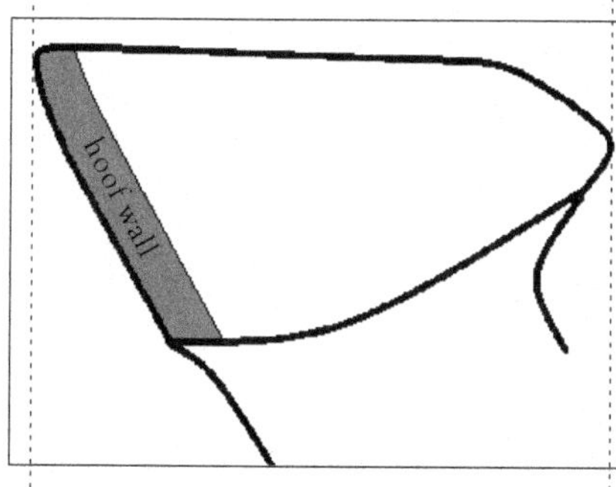

Figure S5-a. This is a simulation of an over grown hoof. VP is flat suggesting the hoof was shod.

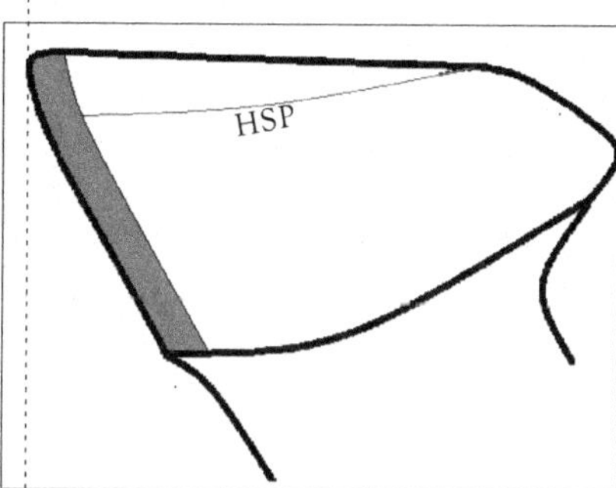

Figure S5-b. Nipper dragging has revealed the juncture of the toe wall with its nearby *hard sole plane* (HSP). A cut-line has been drawn along this juncture with a Sharpie from the toe to the terminal ends of the overgrown heels. Note: compare this drawn line with the line drawn in the next step below on the outside of the hoof wall.

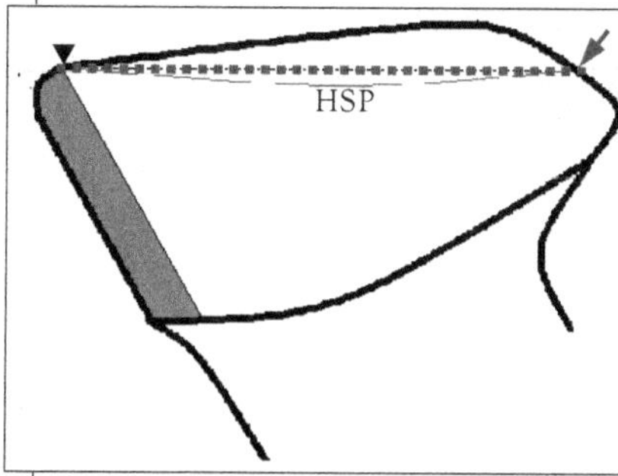

Figure S5-c. The toe wall has been shortened to the HSP. ▼ marks the location of the exposed toe wall pillar. *Blue arrow* points to the MLHA, established by nipper dragging the HSP from the toe to the heels. *Dashed line* is drawn straight across the outer wall; this is a cut-line the trimmer may follow with the outer nipper blade. However, the trimmer uses the HSP as the pre-emptive cut-line for the inner nipper blade to follow; the outer blade will automatically adjust to the cutting path of the inner blade so as not to cut through the hoof wall and into the sole below the HSP.

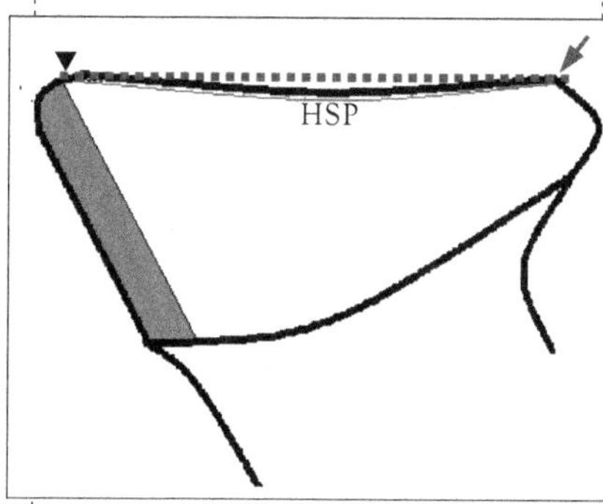

Figure S5-d. The hoof wall has been shortened to the HSP from the toe wall to the heels. *Blue dashed line* marks the cut-line drawn on the outer wall in **Figure S5-c**. Note that the expanse of hoof wall from the MLHA to the toe wall pillar is slightly arched. This follows from the inner nipper blade tracing the HSP. This arch represents passive wear, which is in keeping with the wild horse model for the naturally shaped hoof. The final step is to complete the mustang roll.

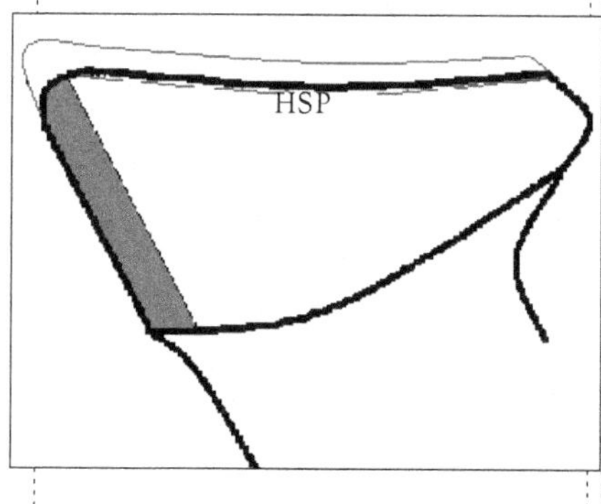

Figure S5-e. *Blue line* marks pre-trimmed hoof

trim to each cut-line. We are half way done!

Step 5: Trimming the ground-bearing surface of hoof wall for the mustang roll

One more task to complete before leaving the bottom of the hoof. This involves trimming the hoof wall to form the *mustang roll* **[Figure P4-2]**.]. This is a fairly complicated part of the natural trim, but with close attention to detail, you can do this with great results. There are three parts to forming the roll: 1) Trimming the hoof wall back to what is called the "water line" **[Figures S5]**– this is done on the hoof stand's cradle or in the 1st Position described in the Sequencing study assignments; 2) Contouring the lower outer wall to mesh with the cut from below – this is done with the hoof placed on the grip head of the hoof stand; and, finally, 3) Refining the nipper work done in #1 above with the HB-2 – the purpose being to accentuate (render "active") the water line (**Step 8**, *below*).

Step 6: Removing excess growth from the outer hoof wall

For the first time, we'll be using the "flat rasp" to trim the hoof. "Excess growth" is any growth of the hoof that would be worn away naturally in the horse's wild state, including the outer hoof wall. Not all parts of the hoof wall have excess growth, but it is unusual for any domesticated horse not to have some

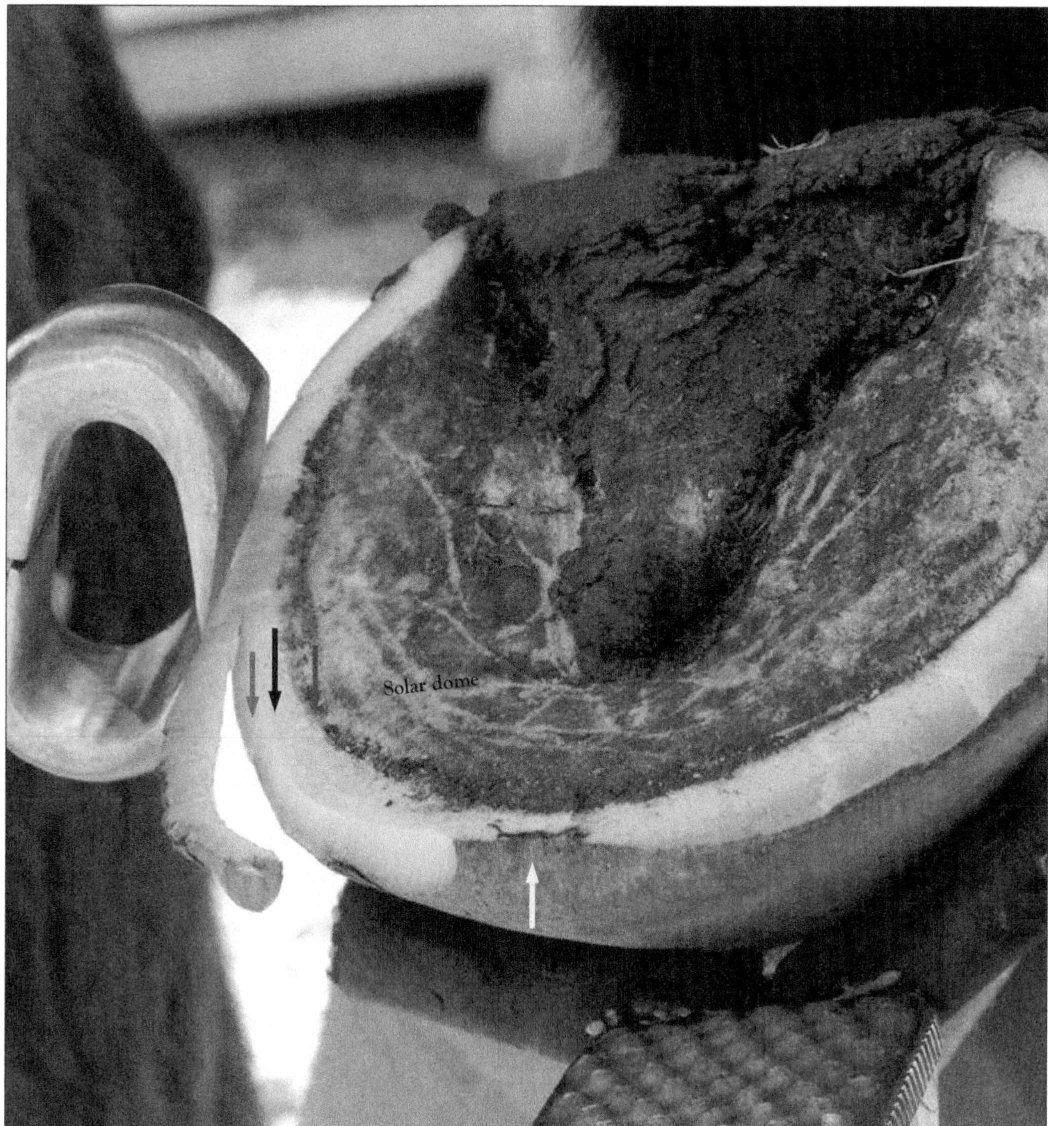

[Figure S5] This is a very important view into natural trim mechanics. The photo is of one of our horses living 24/7 in our Paddock Paradise at the AANHCP Field Headquarters near Lompoc, CA. *Black arrow* points to the *Stratum internum* (innermost hoof wall) – a ring of tough, dry epidermis that nature intends to be there from toe to heel, and which is the most "distal" (closest to the ground) structure of the naturally shaped hoof. The wild horse hoof model teaches us that this is "nature's horseshoe." *Red arrow* points to the most important cut in forming the *mustang roll*: the *Stratum medium* (middle section of the hoof wall) is beveled at the outer perimeter of the *S. internum*. The absence of pigmentation in the *S. internum* tells us precisely where to make the cut. *Yellow arrow* points to a short segment of the mustang roll that I've left untrimmed, and which I am using here as a guide in turning the angle of the mustang roll on either side; later, I will lower this segment into position and alignment with the rest of the mustang roll. *Blue arrow* points to the *Stratum lamellatum* ("white line"), which lies passively to the *S. internum* in the hoof's relative concavity. When a horse is living in a well-planned Paddock Paradise such as ours, and each of these three structures – *S. medium*, *S. internum*, and *S. lamellatum* – are brought into natural alignment with each other, the solar dome and frog will require no trimming. The sole and frog of the hoof has not been trimmed since the horse entered our Paddock Paradise seven years ago in 2010.

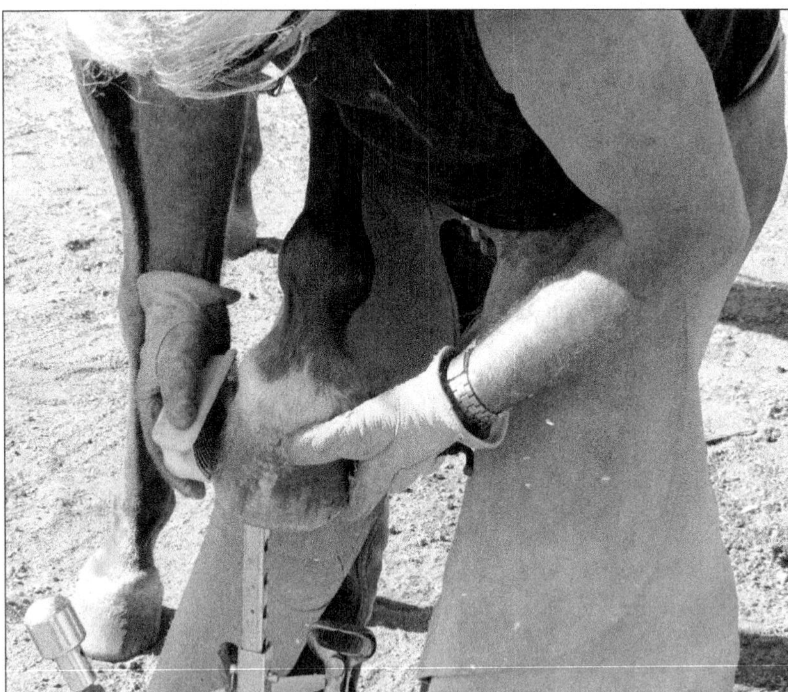

Fine finishing the mustang roll with the RR-1.

excess growth, including at any point on the outer wall. Typically, areas of excess growth occur more over areas of *active wear* than *passive wear*. This is important information for you to keep in mind and it will be a critical area of focus in your work in the cadaver trim clinic.

It should be mentioned also that removing excess growth from the outer hoof wall also contributes to defining hoof wall *symmetry* in front hooves and *asymmetry* in hind hooves. These basic characteristics of the naturally shaped hoof can only be evaluated when the hoof is placed on the grip head (Sequencing: 2nd Position for fronts, 5th Position for hinds) of the hoof stand and evaluated in its superior view. Minor growth irregularities along the lower periphery of the outer wall may be removed with the flat rasp at this time, or skipped and removed in the next step.

Step 7: Trimming the lower outer wall for the mustang roll

With the outer wall cleared of any excess growth, and symmetry or asymmetry confirmed, the time has come to finish the mustang roll that was initiated in Step 5. The RR-2, RR-1, and HB-1 are used in that sequence to complete the roll with the hoof still on the grip head.

Step 8: Accentuating (final finishing) the water line

The hoof is finished with this step. Using the HB-2 in the 1st and 3rd Posi-

Fine finishing the mustang roll with the HB-1.

tions, render any part of the hoof wall "passive" to the water line. This is a relatively simple process, but requires astute attention to detail by the trimmer.

Step 9: Measuring and recording final data (post-trim)

When all the previous steps are complete, the same Critical Measurements gathered in Step 1 are gathered again here. In life (as opposed to a cadaver trim), this is extremely important data that the trimmer will reference at the next trim session to evaluate changes in or stability of the Critical Measurements.

Study Assignments

- **PowerPoint Lecture – "Efficient Shoe Pulling"** – Pulling shoes is not mandatory training, but is useful if no one is around to pull them for you. My standing advice is to have the horse owner's farrier pull them off, but not trim the hooves.
- **The Natural Trim – Chapter 16: "Shoe Pulling"**
- **PowerPoint Lecture – "NHC specialized dissection"** – The purpose of this practicum is to afford students the opportunity to understand the relationship between the dermal and epidermal structures.
- **The Natural Trim – Chapter 15: "Notching the Hoof"**

Step 1 – ISNHCP Training Program

Independent Study Written Exam

This "open book" online exam is given mainly for the ISNHCP's informational purposes so we can assess your preparedness to proceed with your **Cadaver Trim** and **Sequencing Clinics**. The exam focuses primarily on the Independent Study learning materials that are most relevant to our model, trimming, and sequencing. Each question is derived directly from your learning assignments and the content of the Training Manual itself. Further, while we don't expect you to know how to conduct the natural trim, we do require that you know about the natural trim at the level of detail provided in this manual. Questions are straight forward – there are no "trick questions" – covering:

- Wild, free-roaming horses of the U.S. Great Basin as our NHC model:
    - ◊ Relationship to *Equus ferus ferus.*
    - ◊ Why not all "wild" horse populations can serve as the NHC model.
- The major hoof related structures: epidermal, dermal, bones, tendons.
- Use of the Hoof Meter Reader.
- Your understanding of the:
    - ◊ Critical Measurements – H°, H°TL, B°, and B°TL.
    - ◊ Navigational Landmarks – MAVP, MPVP, MATW, MPTW, ⊙, and MLHA.
- *Active wear* and *passive wear.*
- Support triads, Hoof Balance and Heel Balance.
- The horse's *support diagonals* used during sequencing.
- Whole Horse Inflammatory Disease
- Paddock Paradise

Study these materials and you will succeed and move forward to your **Cadaver Trim Clinic**. You can do it!

When you are ready, return to the ISNHCP website, Step 1, and follow the instructions for taking the Independent Study Written Exam.

ISNHCP Training Program
Cadaver Trim Clinic

Following the successful completion of Step 1 ("Independent Study"), students will advance to one of hands-on Cadaver Trim Clinics offered by our clinicians. These run for seven to nine or more days – depending upon the individual clinician and whether or not they are including the Sequencing Clinic as part of their Cadaver Trim Clinic.

The purpose of this clinic is to provide you with trimming experience on cadaver hooves. You will learn to measure, trim, evaluate the hooves for heel and hoof balance, and fill out your data forms.

ISNHCP Cadaver and Live Horse Data Form — This is the data form you will be using throughout your training. It's included in the DVD, so make copies and carry them with you to your clinics and mentorships. Note in the second line of the form that you are required to include your clinician or field instructor's name, and that they are to sign off (initials only) to the right of their name for the cadaver or horse you trimmed. Keep these completed forms. I will want to review them if you clinic with me, and if you intend to apply to the Advanced Natural Trim Training Program, they will be required.

Refer to the ISNHCP website for specific clinic requirements.

ISNHCP Training Program

Sequencing Clinic

Sequencing is an extremely important foundational part of your training. It includes efficient tool and equipment management during trimming; effective and humane horse handling and communication skills; and optimal body positioning of the horse, trimmer and (if participating) handler. Sequencing, in other words, includes those strategically important things that we do that are supportive of the trimmer's efforts to trim the horse. Sequencing is so important in its own right that it is taught separately from trimming until such time that the student is sufficiently skilled and prepared to bring both together in the **Live Horse Trim Clinic**.

Sequencing video submission – Before advancing your Live Horse Trim Clinic, you must produce a video for the ISNHCP to evaluate your sequencing skills. In the video, you must be able demonstrate on one horse that you are physically in shape and can sequence according to clinic standards taught by your clinician and as explained elsewhere in this Training Manual and reading assignments. This confirmation is important because the Live Horse Trim Clinic will require that sequencing is confirmed if you are to trim effectively, efficiently and safely while under the horse. The ISNHCP requests that you create a private Facebook page for your video. After making payment on the ISNHCP website, send a link to the ISNHCP to make the evaluation. Students who cannot sequence to ISNHCP training standards may be required to return to another Sequencing Clinic. If, in the ISNHCP's opinion, only practice is merited, and the student can bring their sequencing to standard without further training, they may petition the ISNHCP to accept a second video at a later date.

Refer to the ISNHCP website for specific clinic requirements.

ISNHCP Training Program
Live Horse Trim Clinic

Upon approval of the sequencing video from the ISNHCP, students will advance to a one or two-day intensive introduction to trimming live horses. In this clinic, students will bring together under a live horse their Step 1 academics, cadaver trimming skills, and sequencing techniques.

About the Clinic – this is a one-on-one training session with your clinician. The clinician will guide you through all the sequencing and trimming steps on one or more horses so that you can return home and safely begin practicing on your own or trusting friends' horses. If you are unable to trim at least one horse for any reason during this clinic you are required by the ISNHCP to schedule additional Live Horse Clinic time until such time as you are ready to practice alone. Your clinician will advise you if you need to schedule additional clinic days or are ready to return home and practice on your own. The clinician's decision will be included in their training report filed with the ISNHCP. Typical reasons for failing the Live Horse Clinic may include any of the following:

- Physically unable to sequence because you have not kept in shape nor practiced.
- Forgot how to measure hooves.
- Unable to trim according to guidelines because you forgot what you were taught.
- Don't use the appropriate tools for any given hoof structure.
- Unable to manage your horse due to poor communication skills with horse.
- Will not follow your clinician's instructions when given.
- Not equipped with all the required tools and equipment.
- Do not fill out required data forms.
- Arrive late, leave early, or don't show up for any reason.

Sequencing & trimming video – Follow the same Facebook submission instructions for the Sequencing video requirement. After submitting your video, make payment on the ISNHCP website to trigger the evaluation process.

Refer to the ISNHCP website for specific clinic requirements.

ISNHCP Training Program

Field Mentorships

Following successful completion of the **Live Horse Trim Clinic**, and approval by the ISNHCP of the Live Horse Clinic video evaluation, students may move forward to the Field Mentorship phase of the training program. The purpose of the mentorships is to give you real life trimming experience with your instructor's client horses. This is an important opportunity to learn how to interact with clients and deal with many different horses you've never trimmed before. This experience will prepare you for trimming your own client horses after you've completed your training.

Refer to the ISNHCP website for specific mentorship requirements.

ISNHCP Training Program

Student Practitioner, Level 1:
Final Written Exam & Final Field Exam

Following successful completion of your final mentorship, your last Field Instructor will advise the ISNHCP if you are ready to take your Final Field Exam. You must also take your Final Written Exam.

Refer to the ISNHCP website for specific examination requirements.

ISNHCP Training Program

Student Practitioner, Level 1: Status on AANHCP website

Following successful completion of both **Student Practitioner, Level 1** written and field exams, students are listed publicly on the Practitioner Locator List of the AANHCP, our affiliate organization's website. Listing on this website is a privilege that honors our model ~ the wild, free-roaming horse of the U.S. Great Basin. Good standing in accordance with the AANHCP's Oath of Allegiance (Oath) and Disciplinary Policy (DP) is a requirement to be listed. The Oath and DP are included with your ISNHCP learning materials (DVD). Be sure to study both of them closely. They are our contracts with you!

As a Level 1 student practitioner, you have several requirements to fulfill before moving forward to Student Practitioner, Level 2; *refer to the ISNHCP website for additional detailed instructions and requirements*:

AANHCP Annual Dues – All ISNHCP students and graduates posted on the AANHCP website are required to pay annual dues.

Case Studies – As a Level 1 student practitioner, you are required to conduct two case studies (one horse per study) demonstrating that you are able to successfully conduct the natural trim without issues for the entire period of one hoof growth cycle ("1 hgc" = nine months to one year). Study horses should be sound ~ not diagnosed as being clinically "lame" ~ from the beginning to the end of the study period. Specific guidelines for the case studies are included in your DVD ("Case Studies Guidelines"). Studies are evaluated by the ISNHCP. After a minimum of nine months (but no more than 15 months of working in the field as a Level 1 Student Practitioner), email the ISNHCP to let us know that your case studies are completed and ready for submission. There is an evaluation fee for your case studies. After paying this fee on the ISNHCP website, submit your case studies according to the guidelines. Case studies that are incomplete or incorrect will be rejected. The ISNHCP will let you know what you will have to do to render them acceptable. You will be required to pay evaluation fees for any resubmitted case studies.

ISNHCP Training Program

Student Practitioner, Level 2 — Final Written and Field Exams

After one year of working in the field and developing a clientele as a Level 1 SP, you are ready to advance to the final phase of your training as a Student Practitioner, Level 2. Successful completion of this training leads to full "Practitioner" status. The SP-L2 training period is one year and includes the following requirements — refer to the ISNHCP website for more detailed instructions:

- Payment of dues to the AANHCP.
- One day clinic with Jaime Jackson (*see ISNHCP website for specific requirements*).
- Final field exam.
- Written report on a topic assigned by the ISNHCP:
    - ◊ Submit your idea or ideas to the ISNHCP by email. The ISNHCP will respond and authorize your idea or recommend others.
    - ◊ Reports should be submitted by email to the ISNHCP in pdf.

Refer to the ISNHCP website for examination and clinic requirements.

ISNHCP Training Program

ISNHCP Practitioner Status

Congratulations on successfully completing the ISNHCP Natural Trim Training Program! For this achievement, you are now accorded full "ISNHCP Practitioner" Status on the AANHCP website's practitioner locator list. ISNHCP graduates continue to have responsibilities as practitioner members of the AANHCP. These include:

- Payment of dues to the AANHCP:
- Compliance with the AANHCP Disciplinary Policy and AANHCP Oath of Allegiance:
- Continuing Education requirements.

Refer to the ISNHCP website for additional detailed requirements:

ISNHCP Training Program

Continuing Education

The complexities of our vital mission extend far beyond the work we do at the horse's hoof. We have all learned from experience and the pursuit of knowledge in our field of endeavor, that the artful science of NHC has no boundaries, and only raises more questions, begging more answers. Like all of nature, it invites each of us to an infinite adventure in discovery and learning. Only a shortsighted person with a closed mind would say, "There is nothing more to learn." We only need to set course, and then seek nature's secrets awaiting us in the vast unknown and unexplored horizons. Recognizing the supreme importance of continuous education (CE) drawn from our own explorations and discoveries, the ISNHCP and AANHCP will put before all of its members opportunities to learn from those who have gone ahead seeking and discovering in the name of our vital mission.

Some of this will be transmitted via new books, bulletins, and academic papers. Some better explained via webinar technology, now at our disposal. And then, when necessary, we must all come together in the clinic format, vis a vis, to learn "hand's on" because that is the only way to get it right. It is our good fortune that our talented cadre of clinicians continues to grow so that the ISNHCP can provide more regional training, sparing members the wearisome travails and expense of international air flight.

Return to the ISNHCP website frequently ~ it is your professional "home" ~ to learn of the latest news, technology, and CE opportunities.

Jaime Jackson

Advanced Natural Trim Training Program

The Advanced Natural Trim Training Program provides advanced training using the same natural trim guidelines used in the foundational "basics" Natural Trim Training Program explained in this training manual. The guidelines, however, are applied to hooves suffering from extreme deformity due to deep pathology stemming from inhumane riding/training practices, devastating surgical interventions, and disease; they also apply to hooves suffering, by any measure of humane care, from extreme criminal neglect.

While the natural trim guidelines of the Advanced training program do not depart one iota from the *basic* natural trim guidelines, certain challenges presented by the deformed hoof require additional clarification of the basic guidelines. This is due to the fact that, in such cases, the principal structures of the capsule – the toe wall, heels, sole, frog, and bars – are typically not even remotely located in their natural positions. Indeed, grid-lining the capsule with the Navigational Landmarks is virtually impossible for the student who is not first confirmed in the basic guidelines applied to relatively naturally shaped hooves. Moreover, the HMR must be used in entirely new ways in order to gather the Critical Measurements. Complicating the picture further, when the initiating trim session is completed, the same structures are still not in their natural positions. One or more years may be required before the hooves appear "normal" again (*facing page*). This is because natural healing changes are complex both in terms of a timeline (i.e., rate of healing) and how capsule mass migrates within that timeline.

For the above reasons, the *Basic Natural Trim Guidelines* (BTG) are referred to as the *Advanced Natural Trim Guidelines* (ATG) as the ATG represent a highly technical and specialized adaptation of the BTG when applied to hooves suffering the deleterious effects of deep pathology and human inflicted trauma.

Students completing the BTG training program must demonstrate exceptional foundational trimming skills, a broad and in-depth understanding of the 4 Pillars of NHC, unwavering and selfless dedication to the AANHCP vital mission, above average writing skills, and emotional and intellectual stamina anchored to an aptitude for dealing with the complexities and challenges of deep pathology. Admittance into the program is by examination. Student BTG training program records are closely scrutinized. Graduates of the ATG training program are accorded special status on the AANHCP practitioner locator list.

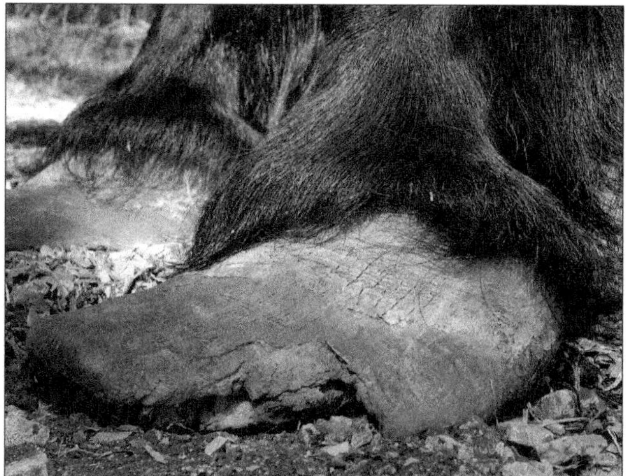

These hooves were part of a 3 year ISNHCP case study. The horse was delivered to AANHCP field headquarters lame from chronic laminitis (i.e., WHID). A plethora of vets, farriers, and barefoot trimmers led the hooves into the catastrophe seen here. Stated simply, no one knew what to do. The third attending vet recommended euthanasia. The owner, referred to me via intermediaries, agreed to make the necessary holistic changes in accord with the 4 Pillars of NHC, including a Paddock Paradise on their 40 acre property.

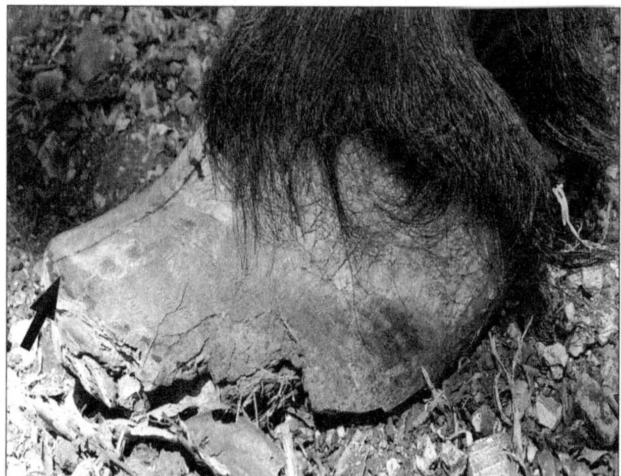

Navigational Landmarks are evident following the first trim run, 2014. Copious amounts of degraded LAM are evident in what is called a "slipper toe" conformation. *Arrow* points to segment of *S. internum*, nearly 3 inches (7.5 cm) above the SP where it would naturally be.

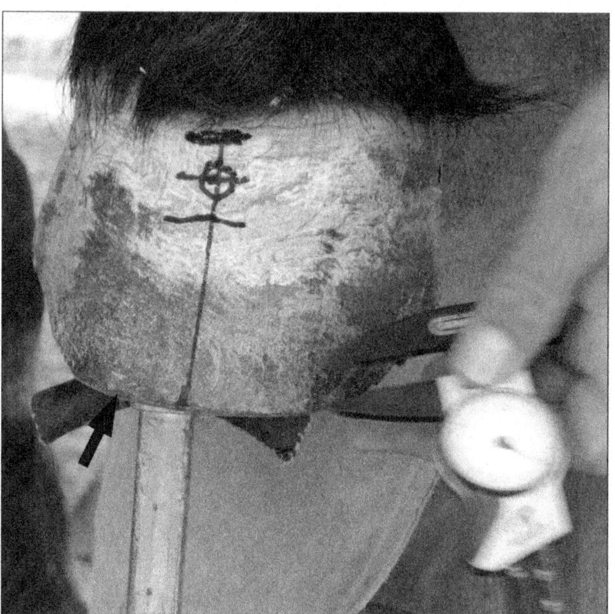

Two years later (2016) the deformity is largely gone, and the horse is completely sound and ridable. *Arrow* points to same segment of *S. internum*, which has finally made contact with the SP. An epidermal wound, not visible behind caliper, triggered by latent toxicity high on the lamellar scaffold has arrived in the hoof's VP. I will wait patiently for repairing enzymes to lyse and cleave degraded mass, supplanted with healthy LAM through restorative keritinization at the basal membrane. ATG students must understand these and other mechanisms, the nature of healing forces described by Hippocrates, calculations of the healing rate, and complex NHC pathways through deep pathology.

Quiz (True or False)
Part 1 — Origins of the Horse and the Natural Trim

1. **Jackson's studies of wild horses included horses living in the U.S. Great Basin, but did not include horses living outside od the U.S. Great Basin.** T – this is important because horses living outside the Great Basin may be living in biomes that do not support the ancient adaptation. For example, I was questioned by a group of horse owners who produced photos of wild horses living on grass pastures in government lands in Washington State, and whose hooves were deformed by excessive growth and inflammation ("laminitis"). I pointed out that they were, in fact, on government lands, but not in the U.S. Great Basin.

2. **The Wild and Free-Roaming Horses and Burros Act of 1971 was the first federal legislation passed to protect America's wild horses.** F – the first act, called the Wild Horse Annie Act, was passed in 1959 which banned air and land vehicles from hunting and capturing free-roaming horses on federal land. The 1971 act prohibited any capture, injury, or disturbance of free-roaming horses and burros on public lands.

3. **The modern horse evolved in N. America over a million years ago, but around 8 to 10,000 years ago, became extinct with many other large mammals. Europeans re-introduced them during the Age of Discovery 500 years ago.** T – the first Europeans to arrive in the Great Basin were Spanish explorers during the mid-1700. But they merely passed through and left no settlements behind, and, while there is genetic evidence of Spanish bred horses in wild horse populations today, there is no record of wild bands of Spanish horses in the U.S. Great Basin a hundred years later when the first Americans settled the area. See next question for further insights.

4. **The first wild, free-roaming horse populations in the Great Basin appeared after 1850, when the region became part of the United States after the Mexican Cessation of 1848.** T – Neither the Spanish nor the Mexicans colonized the area, and it is unlikely that wild horses roamed the Great Basin until after the Americans arrived to settle the area. Likely they brought horses with them that came from other areas of Alta California (e.g., California) that were colonized by the Spanish, and known to have many horses of Spanish breeding.

5. **Jackson's hoof studies at the BLM corrals studied the effects of 125 years of adaptation in the U.S. Great Basin.** F – I only studied the *adaptive form* of the hoof which flourished in the high desert biome of the Great Basin. The actual adaptation took place 1.3 million years ago in North America.

6. **The word "feral" is a human appellation that has little biological meaning except in transitory behavior, usually forced on the animal as when stalled.** T– According to Kirkpatrick and Fazio, "The non-native, feral, and exotic designations given by agencies are not merely reflections of their failure to understand modern science but also a reflection of their desire to preserve old ways of thinking to keep alive the conflict between a species (wild horses), with no economic value anymore (by law), and the economic value of commercial livestock."

7. ***Natural hoof care* and the *natural trim* mean the same thing.** F – From *The Natural Trim*, p. 14, "the reader may be wondering why I am emphasizing the term "NHC" instead of the "natural trim"? Aren't they the same? While related, they have different meanings, and the reader should know what these are. The natural trim refers specifically to trim mechanics, that is, how we physically trim the hoof. It is technically defined as *a humane barefoot trim method that mimics the natural wear patterns of wild horse feet exemplified by wild, free-roaming horses of the U.S. Great Basin.* NHC (natural hoof care), is much broader in meaning and is defined as *the holistic approach to hoof care based on the wild horse model, including natural boarding, natural horsemanship, a reasonably natural diet, and the natural trim itself.*"

8. **NHC can trace its roots to the classic text, *Art of Horsemanship*, written by the Ancient Greek General Xenophon, 350 BC.** T – Xenophon specifically wrote about care of the barefoot horse, including how to toughen their hooves. (P. 15, *TNT*)

9. **Not all wild or feral horse herds are suitable models for NHC.** T – Many free-ranging horses live in environments that foster diseased hooves. (p. 36, *TNT*)

10. **From the standpoint of adaptation, the only distinguishing difference between wild, free-roaming horses of the U.S. Great Basin and a horse living in a stall 24/7 is *experience*.** T – genetically, they are indistinguishable. [p. 34, *TNT*; Also: Kirkpatrick, p. 4, "In another study, Kruger et al. (2005), using microsatellite data, confirms the work of Forstén (1992) but gives a wider range for the emergence of the caballoid horse, of 0.86 to 2.3 million years ago. At the latest, however, that still places the caballoid horse in North America 860,000 years ago. The work of Hofreiter et al. (2001), examining the genetics of the so-called *E. lambei* from the permafrost of Alaska, found that the variation was within that of modern horses, which translates into *E. lambei* actually being *E. caballus*, genetically. The molecular biology evidence is incontrovertible and indisputable, but it is also supported by the interpretation of the fossil record, as well." And Kirkpatrick, p. 4 (last paragraph), "The issue of feralization and the use of the word "feral" is a human construct that has little biological meaning except in transitory behavior, usually forced on the animal in some manner."]

Quiz (True or False)

Part 1 – Naturally Shaped Hooves in the U.S. Great Basin

1. **Front hooves tend to be wider and rounder through the toes than hind hooves.** T

2. **Hind hooves tend to grow at lower angles down the toe than front hooves.** F – Just the opposite in most cases, although some fronts and hinds measured approximately the same.

3. **Jackson found that over 99% of the hooves varied less than 5/8 inches (1.6 cm); and, according to his statistical data curve, nearly 70% varied by less than 3/8 inches (.95 cm).** T – Statistically, this is very little in contrast to what one sees in shod hooves, where some toes are trimmed until the nearby sole bleeds, and others are allowed to grow to fantastic lengths of 7 inches and more, which translates to variations that have no statistical value relative to the natural state of the hoof.

4. **30% of the hooves Jackson studied had hooves that contained some pigmentation, nearly half of those had no pigmentation.** T – My findings stirred great controversy in the hoof care and farrier worlds; in fact, professors at the University of Oklahoma Press, ignoring my findings, rejected out of hand my manuscript for *The Natural Horse* based on the widespread belief that "white" (unpigmented) hooves were structurally weaker than pigmented hooves and could not possibly "select" for the animal's survival in the wild.

5. **Jackson's study found that the hoof's angle of growth, measured in terms of the visible horn tubules of the outer wall, decreased from toe to heel.** T – Another controversial finding because of the equally widespread belief that horn tubules are bundled together in parallel from toe to heel. This finding explains – as you will learn later in your studies – why naturally trimmed horses "walk on their heel bulbs," just like horses in the wild.

6. **Another important finding of Jackson concerned frog pressure. Jackson discovered, as farriers had always contended, that frogs press directly against the ground during the hoof's support phase.** F – I found that the frog always endured passive contact with the ground. Not surprising, this was yet another hotly contested controversial finding, leading to outraged hoof care "authorities" rejecting my entire body of research based on the widespread belief that "frog pressure" against the ground plays an important role in blood circulation. I countered in articles published by the American Farriers Journal, that if frog pressure was so important, why are horses shod, thereby elevating the frog even further away from the ground?

7. **Farriers often "set" toe angle by manipulating heel length and/or toe length with respect to each other, but Jackson's data showed that toe angle has no relationship at all to heel or toe lengths.** T – This find was just about the "final draw" for the farriery community, as my find-

ing basically said we shouldn't be manipulating toe and heel lengths at all, but simply trim them to where nature wants them to be. No one was willing to give up their "gimmicky" manipulations of the hoof and so this important finding remains largely ignored by farriers.

8. **With respect to a hoof's "center line", Jackson found another very peculiar difference between front and hind hooves: front hooves tended to be symmetrical in their bottom and front views, meaning they were divided into two equal left and right sides, whereas hinds tended to be symmetrical in their bottom views but asymmetrical (not evenly divided into left and right sides) in their front views.** T – This is a bit complicated for beginners to follow, but eventually you'll have to figure it out so I'm throwing it into your lap now to wrestle with. Technically, it is an extremely important finding because, once again, it is violated universally by shoers, who shape their hind shoes to be asymmetric because of the illusion of symmetry cast by looking at the hoof from the front. This harms the hoof internally, causing it to grow awry (unbalanced), which NHC advocates like myself have correlated to lameness. For the sake of horses, our vital mission compels each of us to understand symmetry and asymmetry in naturally shaped hooves.

9. **Jackson interpreted the most protruding support points of the hoof wall as areas of "active wear," where descending weight-bearing forces exerted the greatest pressure on the hoof.** T – Another tough one to wrestle with, but eventually you will be trimming hooves to their active wear points of support in the Cadaver Trim Clinic. So the time has come to understand this very important dimension of the naturally shaped hoof.

10. **Jackson did not believe that areas of "passive wear" resulted from hoof wall being worn away, rather that areas of active wear resulted from a thickening of the hoof wall, which he likened to calluses.** T – Another area of hoof form ignored completely by the farrier and vet communities, but which is critical to conducting a genuine natural trim. Conventionally, areas of passive wear along the hoof wall are thought to be of inferior horn quality, and so they simply wear away. But dissections of wild hoof cadavers proved that areas of active wear were simply extra growth built upon the same foundation as passive wear. Further, these "fortified" areas of wall build-up served to balance hooves. The latter is something you will get into shortly – one of the most important things to understand about hoof structure and how you will affect it with the natural trim. As you can see already, this business of "active" and "passive" wear is a big deal in NHC. Don't worry, you'll get it by working hard at your studies here in Step 1, which will also be reinforced when you hit the Cadaver Trim Clinic.

Quiz (True or False)

Part 1 – Research, Experimentation, Birth of NHC Science, and the 4 Pillars of NHC

1. **The natural habitat of the wild horse is a passive player in the natural gaits of the horse, whereas behavior is an active force.** T – (p. 35, *TNH*). The idea here is that although environment is important, behavior driven movement is the principal force that actually shapes the hoof.

2. **Horses do not naturally move backwards.** T – (Table 3-2, *TNH*) Of course, this assertion flies in the face of virtually every equestrian discipline. Yet, I had to report what I saw. Horses just don't go around walking backwards in the wild. They may step back one or two paces to get out of a situation, but that's it. I often put it this way, "There is no horse in the world who, if you were to offer him a bucket of oats 50 feet away behind him, will walk backwards to get there. He'll simply turn around, and then go for it. Biologically speaking, walking backwards beyond a step or two has no survival value to the horse.

3. **Behavior in the horse that is natural, but defiant, will require a "correction" from us to assert our relative dominance, whereas behavior that is malicious signals that the horse is responding from fear to do unreasonable demands having been made upon them, and no correction is warranted.** T – (p. 153, *TNH*) Relative dominance or "RD" is nature's door to the horse's mind. I would not think of having anything to do with horses, except as an observer in wild horse country, if I were deprived of using RD in my relationship with them. Indeed, I believe that horse abuse always begins with a "correction" that is unwarranted. We will use RD during trimming and I will take it up later in this training manual. Understanding natural equine behavior is key to understanding RD.

4. **"Feed Stations" in Paddock Paradise are a way to feed horses that mimics grazing/browsing/foraging behavior – eating small amounts of forage throughout the day – and which stimulates horses to move from one place to the next as they do in the wild.** T – (p. 45, *TNT*) Standing in one place only in order to eat, as in a stall, clashes with our wild horse model for natural feeding behavior.

5. **It is natural for horses led by a monarch alpha male to move from one place to the next in Paddock Paradise, for example, from one feed station to the next, in order of relative dominance.** F – Actually, what happens if there is only one monarch, is what I call an "inversion." Recall from Figure 2-1 in *TNH* that, in the wild, the monarch takes the rear, and the alpha female leads from the front. But in our AANHCP Paddock Paradise with no stallion rivalry, the opposite occurs – our monarch Apollo, takes the lead and all others follow

by lower rank (RD). Alpha monarchs, male or female, are very intolerant of sub-dominant "betas" taking the lead. This relates to the next question.

6. **All stallions are alphas, all geldings are betas.** F – Alpha monarchs are actually rare in the horse's natural world. This applies equally to males and females. They appear to be born that way, in fact, a newborn female alpha will almost immediately begin to pin her ears at others to "put them in their place." Gelding the stallion does not take away his alpha propensities, as it is governed by his individual DNA rather than testosterone.

7. **A "reasonably natural diet" is one that meets the nutritional requirements of the horse, is comprised mainly of "safe" mixed-grass hays, and minor quantities of supplements determined to be safe by the AANHCP. It does not cause laminitis.** T– You've got your reading assignment, *Laminitis: An Equine Plague*, and the time has come to read – and study – the entire book.

8. **WHID is another word for laminitis.** F – (p. 16, *Laminitis: An Equine Plague*) Laminitis is a *symptom* of Whole Horse Inflammatory Disease (WHID).

9. **The three stages of laminitis are *sub-clinical* (symptoms with the absence of pain), *clinical* (symptoms accompanied by pain), and *chronic* (symptoms that are both *clinical* and *sub-clinical*).** T – (p. 23, *Laminitis: An Equine Plague*) It's important for you to recognize all three stages of symptoms. Significantly, if you know the sub-clinical symptoms, you have an opportunity to advise the horse owners to make changes that will avoid the later stages.

10. **Vets have no role in the treatment of laminitis.** F – (p. 89, *Laminitis: An Equine Plague*) Vets play an important role in terms of confirming a diagnosis and prescribing anti-inflammatory medications if appropriate.

Quiz (True or False)

Part 2 – Structures of the Horse's Foot

1. Each hoof has two bars. T
2. The white line lies between the sole and the water line. T
3. The "wings" refer to the posterior processes of P3. T
4. The role of the DDFT is to flex the joints of the foot for flight. T
5. The hoof wall is composed of minute hairs that are "glued" tightly together. T
6. Horn tubules have semi-hollow cores called medulla. T
7. All the epidermal structures are "extruded' by minute *papilla* in the *Supercorium*. T
8. The dermal leaves of the lamellar corium are separated by epidermal leaves. T
9. The heel bulbs are extensions of the frog. T
10. The terminal arch is a vascular structure that connects the digital arteries within the coffin bone. T

Quiz (True or False)

Part 3 – Importance of Measuring

1. **Finding the MPVP is the first step in finding one's way to H°.** F – MAVP is the first step.
2. **The MATW terminates at the crest of the capsule.** T
3. **The bull's-eye is located 1 cm below the crest of the capsule.** T
4. **H° is measured parallel to the MATW segment between the upper (⊙) and lower horizontal lines.** T
5. **The true hoof wall begins at the lower shoulder of the coronary groove.** T
6. **H°TL is measured from ⊙ to the VP.** F – It is measured to the SP.
7. **H°TL is always measured in alignment with MPTW.** T
8. **A hoof is said to be *wry* when the MATW does not align with the MPVP .** T
9. **B° occurs when the MATW is bent by a DTA.** T
10. **A DTA cannot bend the MPTW.** T
11. **A "slipper toe" occurs when the MATW is bent forward by a DTA.** T
12. **B°TL occurs when the MATW is bent by a DTA.** T
13. **The MPTW and MATW always align.** F – Except when the hoof is wried.
14. **H°TL and MPTW always align.** T
15. **Bull-nose conformation occurs when B° > (is greater than) H°.** T
16. **Slipper toe conformation occurs when H° > B°.** T
17. **B°TL is measured from ⊙ to the SP.** F – It is measured to the end of the MATW. Technically, this means where the outer wall terminates at the distal end of the MATW. For example, if the toe wall has a mustang roll, B°TL is measured to where the upper roll begins on the MATW.
18. **H°TL measures shorter with a tape measure than with the HMR if the MATW terminates in a mustang roll.** F – The question is bogus because H°TL, by definition, can only be measured to the SP.
19. **H° is determined by the length of H°TL relative to the length of the heels.** F – In the naturally trimmed and worn hoof, H° is independent of both H°TL and heel length. In other words, the toe wall's natural angle of growth is pre-determined by the horse's DNA.
20. **The MHR is calibrated to my wild horse hoof data.** T

Quiz (True or False)

Part 6 - Hoof Form and Function

1. **The natural gaits aren't the same thing as the natural gait complex (NGC).** T – (p. 128; p. 134) The *natural gaits* speak to the walk, trot, and canter/gallop, which is a very limited way to try to explain how the horse moves. The NGC, in contrast, connects the gaits to the natural behaviors of the horse and the myriad ways that horses actually move using those gaits.
2. **Wild mules can be part of family bands of horses.** T – p. 131
3. **Wild horse family bans occupy well-defined *home ranges*.** T – p. 133
4. **The NHC model for the hoof mechanism states that the "hoof lands, spreads apart a little under the weight of the horses, then springs back together again when the hoof leaves the ground."** F – (p. 135-137) NHC model states the hoof lands and pretty much "locks" in place with little to know flexion of the capsule.
5. **Fluids in the foot's vascular channels under pressure from the weight-bearing force are said to be equalized by the presence of small "shunts" that open and close, connecting the sub-branches of the arteries and veins.** T – (p. 151).
6. **The NHC model for the hoof mechanism states that both P3 and the LAM are non-weight bearing structures during the hoof's support phase.** T – (p. 152). This assertion is considered sacrilege by the generic barefoot, farrier and veterinary communities. But logic says otherwise.

Quiz (True or False)

Part 9 — Sequencing

1. **Treating is important to reinforce cooperative behavior with the horse.** T
2. **Ear radar can tell us where the horse's attentions are.** T
3. **Tail swishing can be a sign the horses is irritated with us.** T
4. **Free-reining is a way to trim the horse without a handler.** T
5. **The diagonal is a significant part of the horse's natural support position** T
6. **When setting the diagonal pressure is applied to the horse's shoulder and may be supported by lead line pressure on the same side.** T
7. **The horse will move backwards each time we set his diagonal.** T
8. **The grip head will slope down in the direction of the toe.** T – At the time *TNT* was written, the grip head was configured to slope upwards towards the toe. The design has changed to facilitate a downward slope.
9. **Light pressure to the horse's stomach muscles tends to lighten and raise the forelimb.** T
10. **Kneeling to trim the hind limb is a violation of sequencing protocol.** T
11. **The correct position of the horse's hind limb above the hock joint is under the trimmer's arm pit during trimming.** T
12. **The MATW is set against the cradle when trimming the hind hoof.** T
13. **Treating and/or praising the horse after every act of cooperation encourages negative behavior.** F
14. **Treating and/or praising the horse at any time does not encourage negative behavior.** F
15. **Setting the diagonal, turns on the hindquarters, turns on the forehand, and side passes are the most direct and efficient ways to position a horse for trimming.** T

Index

Index of Quizzes

CPSIA information can be obtained
at www.ICGtesting.com
Printed in the USA
LVOW06s2328080917
548119LV00030B/1756/P

9 780984 839957